Searching for

Design

with Fibonacci and Phi

by

Dan Harwell

To: P.J.
A beautiful girl
with a vision for
creativity and design-
Fibonacci!
Dan Harwell
1996

Contributions by

Jim Johnson, AIFD

Bob Bigham, AIFD

Osamu Honjo, AIFD

Jennifer Johnson

Raymond Elliott

Gary Norman

Ken McConnico

A GOLDEN SPIRAL PUBLISHING BOOK

ISBN 0-9648677-0-2

Searching for Design
         with Fibonacci and Phi
was produced and prepared by
Golden Spiral Publishing
1842 Matador
Abilene, Texas 79605

Edited by Patty Hundley
Design and production by Imagination ii
Color separations and printing by Quality Printing
Bound by Chapman and Sons

Table of Contents

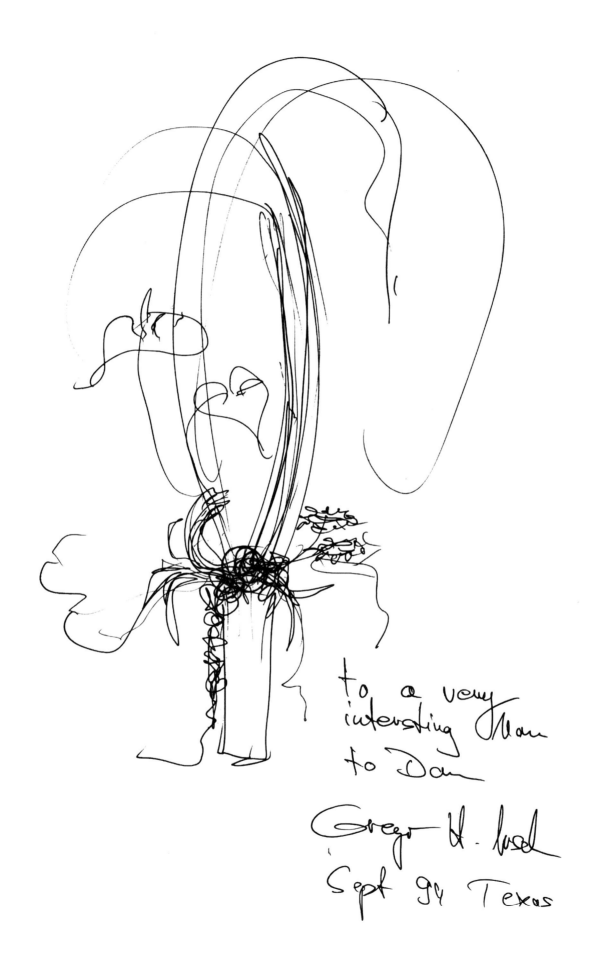

to a very
interesting Man
to Dan

Greg H. Bush
Sept 94 Texas

FOREWARD by Gregor Lersch
International Teacher and Author

A long secret wish became reality!

  The first book concerning the application of the "Golden Cut" through the eye of a florist is here. Nothing has been more fascinating in my career than the learning process of the application of the golden rule to form the natural symmetry, and most of all the asymmetry. The division of colors, the possibilities of shapes, and the mixing within themselves, must agree in logic and mood. This rule has a certain quality that does not limit the personal creativity and after intuitive application and performance becomes describable and most importantly can be learned (acquired) by others. Substances of shapes retain a recognizable formula. Even the creativity itself teaches one to understand oneself, its impression knowingly to modify.

  It gives me great joy that a seasoned specialist, the honorable Dan Harwell from Texas, a successful florist, salesman, and colleague through and through — as the German language says — suddenly took up this topic. His endless depth and importance comes out of the universe to recognize philosophy and psychology and explore this fantastic formula, to study it, and with all his energy to apply it in the floral profession.

  I always enjoyed the serious way with which he conversed enthusiastically with me to retrieve more of my knowledge concerning this topic. I thank Dan for the many days, nights, and all the time he devoted to this project. No reward is too big. Up to now, famous teachers and instructors in this profession have avoided the distinctness of the "Golden Cut," perhaps not being knowledgeable of its importance.

  I wish to evoke my own contribution in regards to this foreward. I am certain Dan Harwell and Jim Johnson, with plenty of spirit, strength, and energy gave the initial push, but as Dan mentioned, it started through me to translate understandably. I believe in the success of this consequently beginning work. America's florists hold something in their hands that is the envy of many colleagues in the world — A golden rule of learning possessing the feasibility to gain success in association with the flower.

  I myself, on my many travels across the world, will inform about the topic, through presentations, demonstrations, and various activities, and show that the great masters, not in vain, considered us florists and made us aware of the topic. Dan made it possible for the florist to become more aware, without the flower losing its magic. I wish all, eager to learn in our profession, would read this book, use it, and apply the utmost importance of it: Proportionality, harmony of color, dimensions, and consequence of shape in association with the plant and flower.

The only answer for many questions from florists? Dan Harwell's new book!!

$\mathcal{F}$OREWARD by Raymond Elliott
Professor of Music and Author

Ladies and Gentlemen: Meet Dan Harwell, Horticulturist and businessman.

While a student at Texas Tech University, Dan rented a room from us. My wife Helen was impressed with Dan's inquiring about a quiet place which would be good for studying. He had well-established goals, backed by strong determination. So he not only moved into our room, but also into our hearts so much so that eventually we called him our "adopted" son. Coming with him were flower pots with growing plants that thrived at his touch, a touch that extended to our beautiful landscaped property with trees, shrubbery, and flower beds. Whether or not I was there, Dan was pruning, digging, fertilizing and watering. He was so much a part of every growing thing that I said to my Helen, "He seems grafted to every shrub and tree, every vine and flower, even to every blade of grass."

Having been denied the guidance of a father, he turned to me for counsel. Together we outlined his career. Dan was in the Air Force ROTC and was a candidate for pilot training upon graduation. His first choice of planes out of pilot training was the C-130, a four-engine turbo-prop cargo plane which would simulate commercial planes after his discharge. With extra days off as a commercial pilot, he could gradually acquire his own business.

It was Dan's ideal plan and worked perfectly until he met lovely Donna just before the last of three tours of duty in Viet Nam. Donna didn't want them to live in the shadow of air accidents and constant travel separations so together they began a search for the perfect job after separation from the Air Force. When he would have an offer, and he got several, he'd call me. I had misgivings about each as did he. They were not Dan, no growing things. Finally there was an opportunity to buy Baack Florists and Greenhouses in Abilene, Texas. "Buy it!" I yelled. "I don't know if I can," he said hesitantly. "Buy it!" I almost ordered, and after three such calls with my repeated "buy it," Dan informed me that he had made a deal with Mr. Baack. He managed to buy the business without any borrowed money by saving flight pay and selling leave back to the Air Force.

Today, 23 years later, Dan owns three flower shops, a nursery and landscaping business, a range of producing greenhouses, and a Christian bookstore. After starting with only himself, Donna and one other designer, he now employs a team of over 50 employees including designers, growers and technicians.

When Dan introduced me to the concept of phi and Fibonacci, I immediately said, "You must write it." He has written it!

Dan Harwell, a decorated Pilot, horticulturist, successful businessman, husband and father of four sons is as genuine as the things that grow for and with him and with which he is inherently in harmony.

Come blend with him.

Raymond Elliott

DEDICATION

To my wife Donna
The perfect example of Phi in both physical
and spiritual beauty
and
To our design creations through nature!
Nathan, Timothy, Luke and Adam.

A Special Thank You

To **Gregor Lersch** and **Raymond Elliott**,

for their encouragement to write and their contributions of the Forewards;

To **Jim Johnson**, AIFD

for his advice, commentary, beautiful designs, and gracious encouragement . . .

He is the kindest man I know;

To **Jennifer Johnson**,

Jim's Daughter, for the incredible artwork and illustrations;

To **Bob Bigham**, AIFD

a world-class designer, artist, educator and my friend;

To **Osamu Honjo**, AIFD

lecturer and teacher of design specializing in nature and Ikebana — a must for this book;

To **Gary Norman** and **Ken McConnico**,

my staff designers, on whom I depend daily for their beautiful design contributions;

To **Gordon Trice**,

America's most creative photographer;

To **Patty Hundley**,

friend, educator and my editor;

To **Debra Warr**,

graphic designer and designer of books — she made it happen!

And to my Business Staff,

for their unending patience, support and encouragement!

$\mathcal{P}$REFACE

The purpose of this book is to help the reader determine why he recognizes beauty and to give him a renewed and fresh understanding about fundamental design and what most of us consider aesthetically beautiful. It is not intended to imply that the ideas in this book are the only way to create an aesthetically pleasing design, therefore resulting in sameness for every designer. One can take this simple principle and be expressive and creative with his own interpretive style. If this principle is used, the designer can be confident that the results will be aesthetically pleasing to most who view the work, and can also be assured of design balance and structural strength.

It is my hope that readers will become more aware and develop a desire to educate themselves about design and its interesting and beautiful history. Perhaps grasping and understanding this simple and significant concept of design will ***throw open the doors of creativity*** for all who dare to walk through!! We have only touched the surface in the past and maybe the best is yet to come.

The principle involving this concept has many possibilities in all types of design including landscape, interior, fashion, cosmetology, photography, and a renewed interest in art, architecture, and music. Many times one must revisit the original and basic concepts to renew oneself with a fresh understanding in order to move forward with the creative process. Perhaps the scientists and inventors of tomorrow need an understanding of this concept and its use in design and creativity so that they can make the discoveries that have eluded them. Heart Disease? A cure for Cancer? Aids research? Industrial fusion?

The world of mathematics has already discovered the benefits of this concept, especially the "hot topic" Fibonacci number series, and there seems to be an increasing interest in many other fields. The floral profession is also ready and waiting for "something new." Perhaps new concepts and design styles have been hidden in the simplicity of the design principle of nature which is discussed in this book.

Finally, this study of design has opened my eyes to the full magnitude of creation. Perhaps our Creator is not the invisible myth that many of us have living within the confines of finite traditional thinking. He is certainly larger than the universe, and has revealed His essence throughout all of His creation!!

Definition of Terms

Fibonacci —

A shortened version of Leonardo Pisana's nickname, Filius Bonacci. He was a brilliant mathematician who lived in the 1200's and rediscovered the logarithmic number sequence which bears his name (Fibonacci): 1,1, 2, 3, 5, 8, 13, 21, 34, 55, 89, 144.... Each succeeding number has a ratio of 1.618... (Φ) and plays an important role in the morphology of life and growth, especially in the human body and botany.

Golden Section —

The point which divides a line segment into two unequal parts that have a ratio of 1.618... larger to smaller, or .618... smaller to larger respectively. This same relationship occurs between the whole and the larger section of the line segment.

Golden Ratio —

The ratio which has a value of 1.618... or its reciprocal .618. This ratio is found between each Fibonacci number, the dimension of the "Golden Rectangle", and the dimension of the "Golden Spiral". It is called phi, (Φ).

Golden Rectangle —

A rectangle that has the ratio of 1:1.618... between its height and width.

Golden Spiral —

The spiral formed when tracing corresponding points of the golden rectangle as it descends harmoniously (*Illus. 2*).

Phi —

The name given to the ratio of 1:1.618..., after the Greek sculptor, Phidaes. He was the architect of the Parthenon and sculptor of many of the ancient Greek statues. All of his works were rich with the ratio of phi, (Φ).

Beauty —

$$\frac{\sqrt{5}+1}{2} = 1.618...$$

Since this book is written for the artist, I take the liberty to use each of these terms interchangeably without going through all the rigors and discipline needed for mathematical proof. The artist will accomplish beauty if phi is applied to the elements and principles of design even though it only has visual validation.

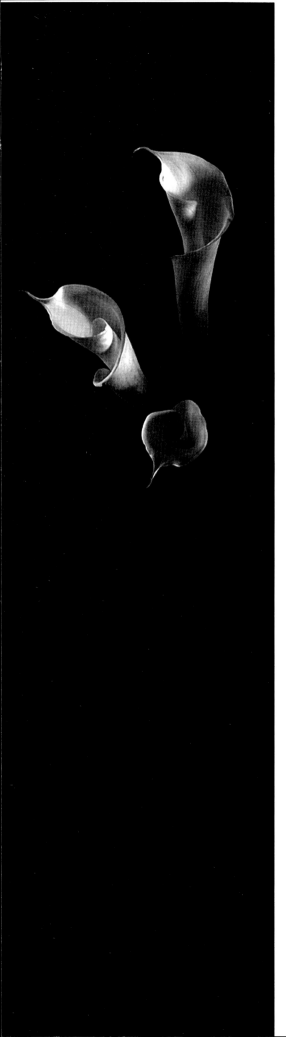

Introduction
Searching for Design

"The secret is 3, 5, 8 ! ! ! Just like your finger is divided at the knuckle, your arm at the elbow, your leg at the knee and your body at the waist, they are all divided at the three and five sections with the overall being eight. This proportion is always pleasing to the human eye."

Not only was I impressed by the simplicity of Gregor Lersch's approach to design when I heard his lecture at the Texas A&M Benz School of Floral Design, but I was intrigued by the association of aesthetic design to human proportion.

Lersch also explained that these numbers were part of the Fibonacci sequence, a number series which nature uses to achieve design balance. Any three consecutive numbers in the Fibonacci sequence can be used and always seem to translate into aesthetic beauty. For example: 3, 5, 8, . . .13, 21, 34, . . .are all Fibonacci numbers and part of the logarithmic sequence found in many elements of design. All sequential numbers in the series are proportionately equal and produce similar design results.

For the first time in my career, as a businessman/ horticulturist operating three flower shops and a range of

greenhouses, I had a glimpse of one of the important "secrets" of design. Oh, I could copy a picture or even follow a formula and I could always tell, as most of us can, when the design was right; but I did not have the real magic touch of an artist nor could I initiate the beginning of a design like the naturally talented creative person. It is this person who does not need a formula for designing; he can see it and create it without having to know why and he can be found not only in the floral industry, but also in artistry, architecture, music, mathematics, and many other professions.

Thus, it was Lersch's revelation that inspired me to learn all I could about design and creativity. I now had a simple understandable foundation which made sense. I found that even the more complicated Ikebana, Japanese design, which looks to nature for its guide, was very similar to that of the mathematical Germans.

I have been driven by this intrigue to make this Search for Design and it has taken me on one of the most exciting adventures and learning experiences of my life. After being encouraged to "shut up and write" by two respected educators/authors, Gregor Lersch of Germany and Raymond Elliott, Professor of Music at Texas Tech University, I can hardly wait to share with you the discoveries of my adventure. I promise this book to be an exciting experience and, perhaps, it will reveal to you the **greatest secret of design**.

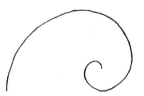

$\mathcal{F}ibonacci \ and \ the \ \mathcal{R}abbits$

1+1=2

2+1=3

3+2=5

5+3=8

8+5=13

(1)

$$\Phi = \frac{\sqrt{5}+1}{2} = 1.618... \ = \ \text{BEAUTY}$$

1
1
2
3
5
8
13
21
34
55
89
144
233
377
610
987
1597
2584
4181
6765
10946
17711
28657
46368
75025
121393
196418
317811
514229
832040
1346269
2178309
3524578
5702887
9227465
14930352
24157817
39088169
63245986
102334155
165580141
267914296
433494437
701408733
1134903170

In 1202, at the age of 27, Leonardo Fibonacci wrote:

"Someone placed a pair of rabbits

in a certain place enclosed on all

sides by a wall to find out how many

pairs will be born in the course of

a year. It being assumed that

every month a pair of rabbits

produce another pair and that

rabbits begin to bear young two

months after their own birth."

When he counted the rabbits at the end of each month, he came up with the following number sequence:

1+1=2, 2+1=3, 3+2=5, 5+3=8, 8+5=13,

13+8=21. . . or, 1, 2, 3, 5, 8, 13, 21, 34,

55, 89,144, 233, 377, 610, 987, 1597,

2584 . . . .

Each number in the Fibonacci sequence is the sum of the previous two numbers and the ratio between each when dividing the smaller into the larger is equal to 1.6180339. . . .*

* Before the 14th sequence the ratio is very close to 1.618. . . or **phi**. After the 14th sequence the ratio is equal to phi. The reciprocal ratio, dividing the larger number into the smaller is .618 . . . .

This ratio between each number is called phi, **Φ**. It is found between the small and large parts of a finger divided at the knuckle, the arm divided at the elbow, the leg divided at the knee, the entire body divided at the waist, and even the face divided at the eyes *(Illus. 3 & 4)*. These Fibonacci numbers and the ratio of phi are found throughout nature in both plants and animals and are the foundation for the beginning of my *Search for Design*.

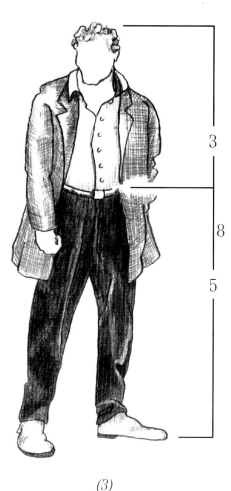

(3)

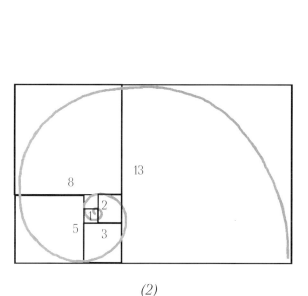

(2)

This diagram illustrates the Golden Spiral of Nature which is formed by a succession of rectangles with logarithmic Fibonacci proportion. The ratio of phi is reflected in the dimension of the rectangles and throughout the logarithmic spiral.

(4)

(5)

"... here and elsewhere we shall not obtain the best insight into things until we actually see them growing from the beginning. ..."

Aristotle

CHAPTER I
Design in Nature

The spiraling wind blows, the fertile soil shifts and the seeds settle. Rain drops moisten the earth and life springs forth to meet the warm sunshine and be rewarded with growth. This is the beginning of a cycle that brings us ultimate creativity, beauty, and balance. All of us would agree that nature's designs are always more interesting and beautiful than anything man can create through art, architecture, or science. What most of us are not aware of is that nature utilizes phi and the Fibonacci numbers in many, if not most, of its creations.

When I first heard about the Fibonacci concept of design and how it could be compared to human proportion, I never in my wildest imaginations realized the intensive role that this beautiful concept played in nature's creation.

My search for design has taught me that the Fibonacci sequence and phi are expressed in plants, animals, and even physical formations throughout the universe. However, life-forms on earth are by far the most visual and prolific in showing off this beautiful

Phi Family

$$\Phi = \frac{\sqrt{5}+1}{2} = 1.618...$$

$$\frac{5}{3} = \frac{8}{5} = 1.6$$

(6)

16

mathematical concept of design.

Phi and the Fibonacci number sequence are found in growth patterns and shapes that most of us notice and consider aesthetically beautiful. For example, many trees use three and five proportionately for the trunk and foliage with the overall size being eight *(Illus. 7)*. Even the saguaro cactus divides and branches proportionately using phi *(Illus. 8)*.

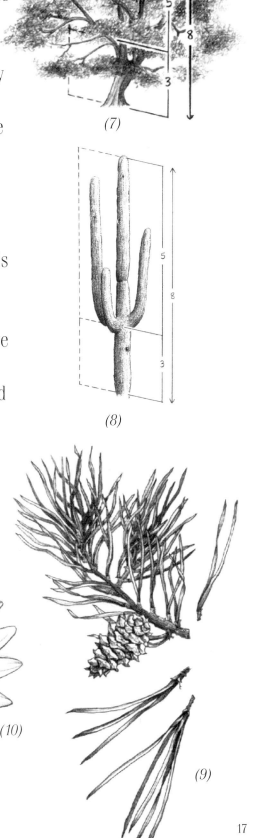

(7)

Pine needles grow in clusters of two, three, or five (all Fibonacci numbers) depending on the species *(Illus. 9)*; daisies have 21, 34, 55 or 89 petals *(Illus. 10)*; sunflowers grow seeds 34, 55, 89, and 144, and these seeds develop in beautiful double spirals, sometimes called spiral mirabilis (miraculous spiral) *(Illus. 11)*. This double set of equal-angular spirals is intertwined, one right-handed and the other a left-handed, with each flower floret belonging to both spirals. Nature must have liked what phi was doing for the sunflower because she continued using the beautiful ratio in the number of seed spirals. Each set of spirals is a sequential Fibonacci number, 21 clockwise and 34 counter-clockwise. Other very similar opposing spirals associated with Fibonacci numbers are also found in the pine cone, with five and eight spirals, and in the pineapple with eight and thirteen.

(8)

(11)
See Illus. 2 & 41

(10)

(9)

Formal Linear — Interpretive Design

Few specimens in the plant kingdom offer such dramatic proof of the golden spiral as this newborn tropical fern frond! Even its protective pubescence cannot conceal the tremendous energy about to unfurl. This composition has an all-star cast. There are no secondary players — only a few stagehands (ming and galax) are there to cover mechanics. Each form floats in space while the connecting lines draw the eye in a counter-clockwise path bringing full attention to each one in turn.

Every facet of this composition involves phi: height, width, diagonal axis, material types, and use of color and texture.

Proportion:

Container = 3		Depth = 3	
Material = 5		Width = 5	
Overall = 8		Height = 8	

And color:

Green = 3
Red = 5
Russet = 8

And texture:

Fuzzy = 3
Velvety = 5
Waxy/smooth = 8

Materials:

Spiraling ferns = **Φ**
Spiraling veins on Anthurium
    Spathe = **Φ**

Even the demarcations of future seeds on the Spadix are arranged in the Golden Spiral (*Illus. 41*).

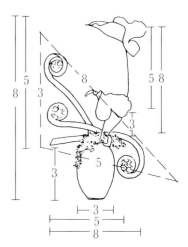

J. Johnson

While it is not surprising that this logarithmic spiral is one of nature's most common patterns, it is also believed to be one of the most beautiful of all curves, and it expresses Fibonacci and phi throughout (*see Golden Spiral page 31*). Nature's spiral is found in a parrot's beak, a nautilus sea shell, a ram's horn, the trunk of an elephant (*Illus. 12-15*), a chameleon's tail (*Illus. 42*), a loin's claw (*Illus. 76*) and the fiddle-head fern (*page 18*). Also, man has not been left out when it comes to this beautiful spiral. The muscle fibers of the human heart and cochlea of the ear form this same logarithmic spiral of nature (*Illus. 16, 17*). Even the very fibers from which we are made, DNA, utilize phi*.

(12)

(13)

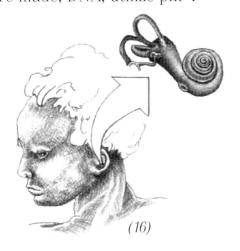

(16)

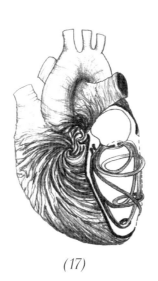

(17)

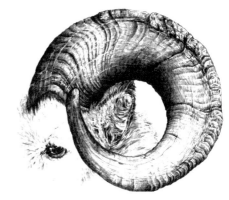

(14)

(15)

* *"Artists and designers have periodically explored the natural and biological principles of design and order in nature. More recently these principles have clearly been manifest in many growth forms but an example of which is the double-helix structure of the DNA molecule, which has the logrithmic proportion of the Golden Section."*
    Harold J. McWhinnie
    University of Maryland

"In DNA, the ratio of the length of period, the height of a representative slice, of the double helix to the width of the double helix and the ratio of the width to the vertical offset of one helix from the other is always very close to Phi."
    T.P. Srinivansan
    School of Physics
    Mapurai Kamaraj University

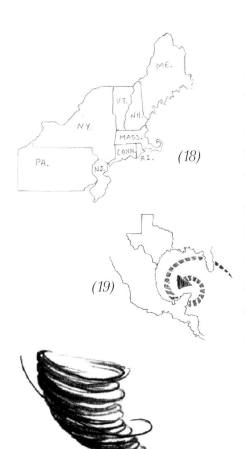

(18)

(19)

This amazing spiral, which is most common in the life forms of plants and animals can also be found throughout our earth. The shore lines of Cape Cod *(Illus. 18)* and the Gulf of Mexico *(Illus. 19)* form this spiral, the same as ocean waves, tide and wind currents, weather and cloud patterns, hurricanes and tornadoes *(Illus. 20)*. And, can you believe nature's beautiful spiral is even found throughout our universe as in the occurrence of craters or dark areas on the moon *(Illus. 21)*, the tail of the comet, and the beautiful spiral of the galaxies *(Illus. 22)*, each of which magnificently expresses nature's ratio of phi?

(20)

(21)

(22)

The plant kingdom's prolific use of phi is also displayed in the faces of its most significant and lovely creation, the flower. The star-shaped periwinkle and petunia *(Illus. 23)* are two obvious examples of these beautiful creations; however, with careful observation, phi can be found in almost every flower. For example, the rose family is based on a symmetry of five, and most flowers with this symmetry have edible fruit. Also, many of the exotic flowers such as the orchid and passion flower, symbolizing love, have a symmetry of five and gloriously demonstrate beauty and phi.*

(23)

* *Because of the appearance of phi in the star-shaped pentagram (Illus. 43), phi is easily found in all flowers with a symmetry of five.*

(25)
Fibonacci numbers appear in the leaf distribution around a central stem: 5 leaves every 3 turns.

(24)
The apple blossom has a symmetry of 5, signifying edible fruit.

Ikebana — Moribana Style

This utterly simple and natural placement of flowers, the way they grow in nature, is the forerunner of our present-day vegetative style design. The Japanese even appreciate a dead leaf in the design as it shows a part of the plant's life cycle. Phi is present in the vertical placement of the iris and even in the formation of the iris buds:

The central cluster = 3
The right cluster = 5
The left cluster = 8

The placement of each cluster into an asymmetrical 3–5–8 triangle:

The overall composition fits within the Golden Rectangle.

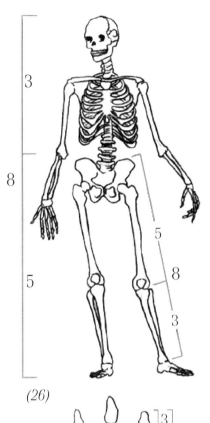

(26)

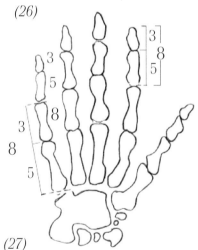

(27)

Phi is also found in bud formations, branching patterns and even in the shapes of leaves. All of these botanical characteristics demonstrate some of the most impressive examples of mathematical beauty found in nature and I find it incredible that nature's favorite ratio is almost always present in some form.

This interesting relationship of phi, which is found in so many areas of nature, did not exclude man in the distribution of this mathematical proportion. Some examples of this inclusion have already been mentioned, but more attention must be given to the revelation of nature's beautiful proportion in man. This discovery revealed to me that I needed to search no farther than my own body to find nature's important and significant secret of design. The relationship of man and phi is most visible in his skeletal proportions and his face. A description explaining the influence of nature's ratio on man is found in Illustrations (26 - 30). These illustrations demonstrate an "extraordinary symphonic commodulation" in nature's design theme.

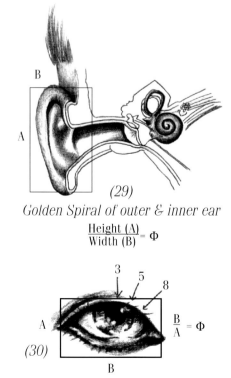

(29)

Golden Spiral of outer & inner ear

$$\frac{\text{Height (A)}}{\text{Width (B)}} = \Phi$$

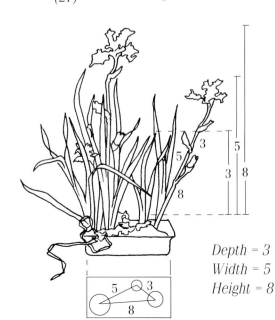

B. Bigham

Depth = 3
Width = 5
Height = 8

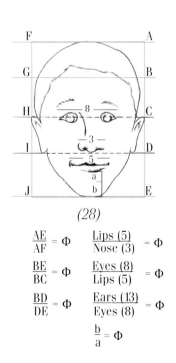

(28)

$$\frac{AE}{AF} = \Phi \qquad \frac{\text{Lips (5)}}{\text{Nose (3)}} = \Phi$$

$$\frac{BE}{BC} = \Phi \qquad \frac{\text{Eyes (8)}}{\text{Lips (5)}} = \Phi$$

$$\frac{BD}{DE} = \Phi \qquad \frac{\text{Ears (13)}}{\text{Eyes (8)}} = \Phi$$

$$\frac{b}{a} = \Phi$$

$$\frac{B}{A} = \Phi$$

(30)

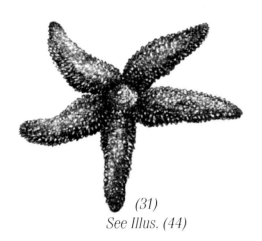

(31)
See Illus. (44)

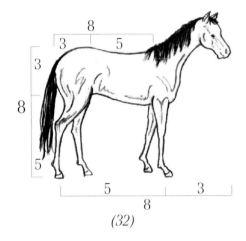

(32)

(33)
Einstein

Furthermore, many sea creatures such as the starfish *(Illus. 31)* and other echinoderms reflect phi as well as the land animals *(Illus. 32)*. Even the ratio of males to females in a honey bee hive is delineated by phi and the Fibonacci number series.

Through the ages, botanists, philosophers, mathematicians, and artists have been good at finding nature's patterns, but it is doubtful that we have yet understood all their causes or even why we like them. We can all wonder whether nature is understandable through mathematical thinking or if we understand her through instinct? Whatever the case, I must agree in part with an article by Robert Lawler in the periodical, <u>Parabola</u>, which indicates that it may be wrong to say that phi could be found everywhere throughout nature; however, Lawler says, "Wherever there is an intensification of function or a particular beauty or harmony of form, there phi will be found." I am convinced that nature not only knows this simple mathematical concept of design, but uses it continually in her creations.

"Nature is governed by the unseen hand of physics and mathematics."

Rolf Sinclair

"Our experience hitherto justifies us in believing that nature is the realization of the simplest conceivable mathematical idea."

Albert Einstein

CHAPTER II
Phi: "The Golden Proportion"

Phi has been called the ratio of Phidias or, simply, phi (Φ) from the first letter of the name of the Greek sculptor, Phidias. This ratio which nature has used so extensively and which is expressed numerically as 1 : 1.618, has many applications in mathematics as well as in design. Nature's beautiful ratio, as well as the ratio of the Fibonacci numbers, is also referred to as the golden ratio, golden section, golden rectangle, and golden spiral, or simply the golden cut, golden mean or golden proportion. The following paragraphs and diagrams will describe and illustrate how phi is found in each of these geometrics. I challenge you to look for beauty and creativity in these illustrations.

Phidias was the architect, designer and sculptor of the Parthenon, the building which is described as having perfect proportion.

(35)

K. McConnico

Decorative - Interpretive Waterfall Design

Implied motion is felt moving through the swan's Hogarth curve neck (double spiral) and into its golden spiral breast. The flowing pattern of feathers carries the eye on into the floral waterfall. This is a great example of a container that "shows the way" to design. Phi is clearly visible in the horizontal proportions:

Container = 3
Floral extension = 5
Total length = 8

Golden Section

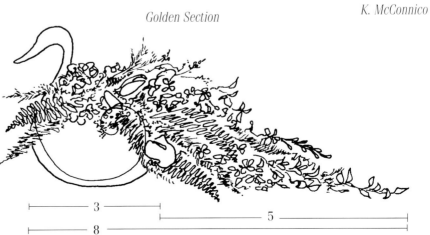

26

GOLDEN SECTION

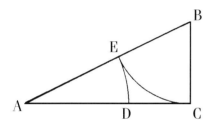

$$\frac{A}{B} = \frac{C}{A} = \mathbf{\Phi} = 1.618...$$

$$\frac{B}{A} = \frac{A}{C} = .618$$

(36)

The golden section is formed when any line segment is divided in such a way that the ratio of the smaller segment (B) to the larger segment (A) is equal to the ratio of the larger segment (A) to the whole (C). This ratio is also called the golden ratio and is equal to phi, **Φ**, 1.618 or its reciprocal .618.

An interesting note: A runner's relay baton is usually held near the golden mean for balance. A drum major's baton is held the same for balance. How about the wings of an airplane? They are seldom placed in the middle, rather always off-center near the golden mean. Even the knob on a door is always very close to the golden mean; it looks right and feels right.

How to find the Golden Section:
1. AC = straight line
2. Draw BC = $\frac{AC}{2}$ perpendicular to AC
3. Connect A B
4. With center B, radius BC, draw arc EC
5. With center A, radius AE, draw arc ED
6. Point D = Golden Section of AC

ex:
AC = 16 Total length
16 ÷ 1.6 = 10 = AD
16 - 10 = 6 = DC

(37)

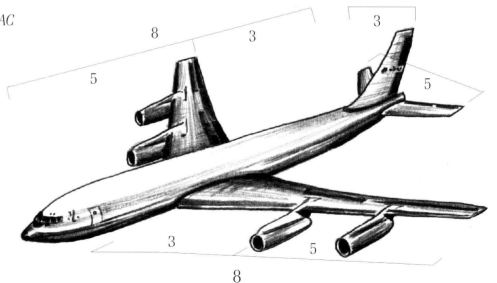

(38)

The Golden Rectangle

J. Johnson

Decorative Parallel Design

This magnificent pair of Chinese treasure chests call for a parallel presentation with decorative elements. When lifting such a lid one *expects* to find real treasures - hence the unique floral components:

Calathea lutea (Havana Cigars)
"Tulip" Anthurium
Peony
Solidaster
Equisetum

Since the flower forms and colors demand attention, phi is not so easy to see, but it is expressed in several ways:

In width:
    Small chest = 3
    Large chest = 5
    Total width = 8
In volume:
    Center = 3
    Right side = 5
    Left side = 8
In flower forms:
    Anthuriums = 3
    Peonies = 5
    Calathea = 8

The banded equisetum placed on the diagonal relieves the "orderliness", produces tension, and implies the golden rectangle.

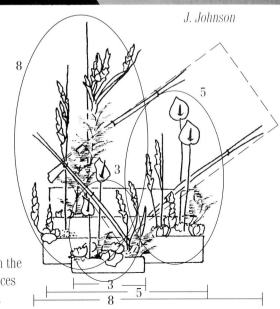

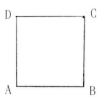

1. *Draw square (ABCD).*

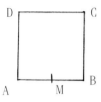

2. *Find midpoint (M) of side (AB).*

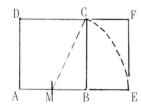

3. *Extend side (AB) with compass to point (E) so that (ME) = (MC).*

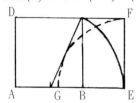

4. *Rectangle AEFD = Golden Rectangle.*
5. *Divide (AB) into Golden Section, use compass to find point (G) on (AE) so that EF = EG.*

$$\frac{AG}{GB} = \Phi$$

$$\frac{AB}{BE} = \Phi$$

(39a)

(39b)
A succession of Golden Rectangles.

GOLDEN RECTANGLE

The golden rectangle is believed to be more aesthetically beautiful than other rectangles. The dimensions of this rectangle will always express phi or the golden ratio between its height and width. Illustration (39a) demonstrates a procedure for finding the Golden Rectangle using a compass.

NOTE: Have you ever seen a square car? Rectangular cars are aesthetically appealing to us, perhaps because they are very close to the eye-appealing golden rectangle. Some of the most beautiful architecture ever constructed utilized this rectangle. The Parthenon is the most famous example *(Illus. 40)*.

"The golden section is an idea used by the creator to generate the similar from the similar."
Johannes Kepler (1611)

(40)

Finding the Golden Spiral

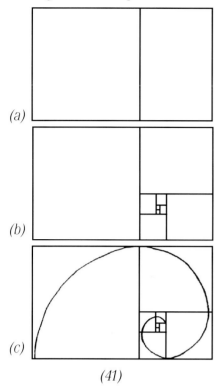

(a)

(b)

(c)

(41)

Interpretive Geometric Design

A spiral of exact stem placement forms the golden spiral - the nautilas shell. Energy from the King protea 'hub' literally pushes the other flowers outward into the gradually opening spiral. Very contrived. Very distinct. Very new!

Phi is expressed in:

Line:

Golden Spiral = Φ

Color:

Pink = 3
Hot Pink = 5
White = 8

Form:

Protea = 3
Roses = 5
Larkspur = 8

J. Johnson

GOLDEN SPIRAL

If the golden rectangle *(Illus. 41a)* is divided to form a square at one end, a new golden rectangle is produced at the other end.

Repeating this process produces a succession of golden rectangles as small as the eye can see *(Illus. 41b)*. Drawing a connecting line through the succession of rectangles produces a logarithmic spiral, which expresses the Fibonacci sequence and phi throughout as shown in Illustration (41c). This simple beautiful spiral is also known as the golden spiral and is found throughout nature and the universe.

"Simple principles are alone productive and it is worthy of remark that the more simple they are the more beautiful and varied their ultimate results."

Viollett Le-Due

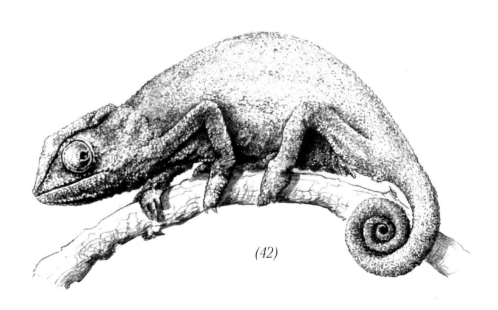

(42)

Golden Triangle

This beautiful traditional design has the form of the Golden Triangle which express phi in height and width. The materials are also distributed in such a way that they form two 3-5-8 asymmetrical triangles within the whole. What a wonderful expression of beauty through the influence of phi.

Proportion:
> Depth = 3
> Width = 5
> Height = 8

or

> Container = 3
> Arrangement = 5
> Overall = 8

Form:

Overall: Golden Triangle = Φ

Material Forms:
> Begonia = 3
> Liatris = 5
> Sunflower = 8

Golden Spiral:
> Begonia Foliage
> Sunflower

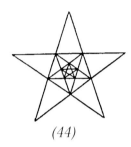

(43)

$$\frac{AB}{CB} = \frac{CB}{AC} = \frac{AC}{DC} = \Phi$$

(44)

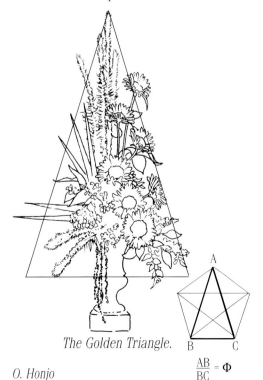

(45)

Pentagram, Pentagon, Golden Rectangles, Golden Triangles and phi.

The Golden Triangle.

O. Honjo

$$\frac{AB}{BC} = \Phi$$

PENTAGRAM STAR

Probably the most expressive of all geometric shapes displaying phi and the golden section is the star-shaped pentagram. Most of us learned to draw this interesting geometric figure at a very early age and were intrigued by the simplicity and beauty in the commodulation of three triangles in which all intersecting lines reflect phi *(Illus. 43)*. This geometric star is full of aesthetically pleasing triangles and rectangles, and it is a shape that expands harmoniously from the interior to the exterior *(Illus. 44)*.

(46)

Man, the pentagram and phi.

Interpretive Design

This design interprets the use of
geometric forms in a new way – super-imposing
a rectangle and a triangle on a circle. A new
concept! Phi makes this design sing:

Proportion:

Depth = 3
Width = 5
Height = 8

Space:

Circular division = Φ
Circle A = Circle B = Φ

Color:

White = 3
Green = 5
Golden Brown = 8

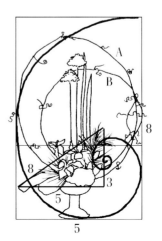

B. Bigham

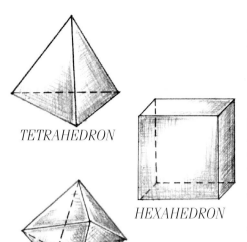

TETRAHEDRON

HEXAHEDRON

OCTAHEDRON

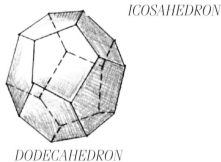

ICOSAHEDRON

DODECAHEDRON
(47)

PLATONIC SOLIDS

The platonic solids are five of the most interesting geometric shapes to be closely tied to phi and the golden proportion. Plato used these beautiful geometric shapes to describe the fundamental laws of the universe in his writing of <u>Timaeus</u>. These figures are defined geometrically as solid figures which divide the surface of a circumscribed sphere into equal parts. It is believed that these are the only five solids which make it possible to divide the surface of a sphere into equal parts.

The mathematics of the phi relationship within these five solids are more complicated than is necessary for us to discuss in our search for design, but the beauty, balance, and interest that these shapes radiate can be an inspiration for all of us. I challenge you to consider and study each geometric individually and then observe how they relate to each other when the five solids are placed one inside the other. This maze-like construction is likely to reveal many interesting shapes and perhaps a new concept of design. *(Illus. 48)*

"The important point for us to observe is that all these constructions and the laws connecting them can be arrived at by the principle of looking for the mathematically simplest concepts and the link between them."
Albert Einstein

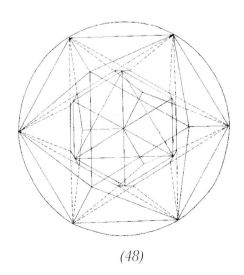

(48)

$$\Phi = \frac{\sqrt{5}+1}{2} = 1.618 = BEAUTY$$

(49)

CHAPTER III

Phi: "The Historical Perspective"

Fibonacci, three-five-eight, golden ratio, rectangle, triangle, spiral. Who was first to use this ratio? When and how is it used today?

When I began my adventure, I started my search with Fibonacci who lived in the 1200's. I soon found that Fibonacci was inspired by Pythagoras, (580 B.C.), the father of mathematics. He was drawn to the idea of the golden section and used the star-shaped pentagram as a secret symbol that identified his followers. Fibonacci's number series, which utilizes the golden ratio throughout indicates that he too was possibly drawn to the golden section and phi.

Pythagoras and his students, the Pythagorians, were probably the first to write about the golden section and its ratio. It is believed, however, that he learned about phi from the ancient Egyptians during his travels through the east. The Egyptians who created the great pyramid, Cheops (4000-2000 B.C.) *(Illus. 49)*, actually used the golden section in calculating measurements for construction. This relationship would naturally contribute to the aesthetic beauty and appeal of the pyramids. Illustration (50) describes the squaring of a

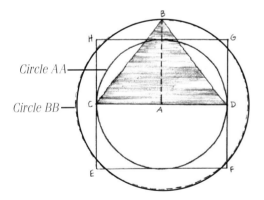

Circle AA

Circle BB

1. $\dfrac{Area\ BB}{Area\ AA}$ = Φ

2. *BC = 1 AC = .618 = Φ*

3. *AB = $\sqrt{1.618}$*

4. *Circumference circle BB =*
   Perimeter EFGH

(50)

circle which uses phi in calculating measurements for the pyramid. This same relationship which identified phi to the pyramids appeared one thousand years later in another religious/scientific monument – Stonehenge. Illustration (51) explains its similar relationship to the pyramids. The golden section even gave Plato suggestions for the foundation of knowledge, and Aristotle drew ethical analogies from it. Galileo said, "God geometricises continually."

Furthermore, the Parthenon *(Illus. 53)*, (400 B.C.), considered by many to be one of the most aesthetically beautiful buildings ever constructed, is probably the most famous architectural design which displays phi and the golden rectangle throughout, even in the minute molding around the crown.

Then, in 1200 A.D., Fibonacci came up with his famous "rabbit" experiment which gave us the Fibonacci number series and the three-five-eight of design. Also, during the middle ages some of the greatest mathematicians, artists, and musicians used the golden section and its ratio in their work: Mozart *(Illus. 52)*, in his composition, <u>Symphony in G Minor</u>; Leonardo De Vinci in his painting, <u>Mona Lisa</u> *(Illus. 60)*; and Franciscan Monk/mathematician, Luca Pacioli, in 1509, who ascribed mystical and metaphysical properties to phi in his book, <u>Divina Proportione</u> (1509), which was also illustrated by Leonardo De Vinci.

As the world moved into the scientific and mechanical ages, less emphasis was placed on the search for true reality, divine reason, and rational thinking. Now that man has invented about everything possible and has complicated and confused what is left, there seems now to be a shift back to the basics to rediscover the who, why, and how.

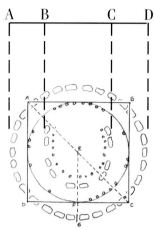

$AB : BC \approx \Phi \approx .618$
$BC : CD \approx \Phi \approx 1.618$

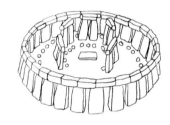

(51)
Stonehenge is a prehistoric British monument which displays precise astrological calculations.

(52)
Mozart

Because of this shift, it is not surprising that the most sensational topic in the field of mathematics today seems to revolve around Fibonacci and his number sequence. This simple concept of design and beauty is appearing everywhere in our society – not only in design, but also in economics, psychology, computer technology, physics, and even religion. Though most of us are unaware, we use the golden ratio in many areas of our lives daily. Our use of this beautiful proportion, however, is most evident in architecture, art, music, and mathematics.

(53)

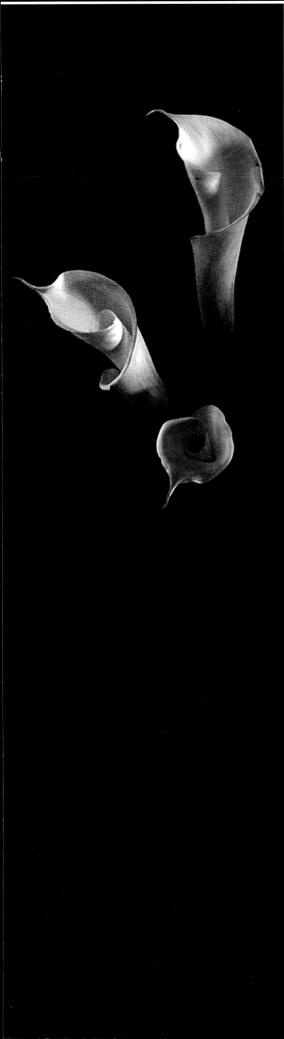

CHAPTER IV

Understanding Beauty

Definition:

Beauty – *"Something which induces immediate and disinterested pleasure."*

Webster

– *"The quality attributed to whatever pleases or satisfies in certain ways as by line, color, form, texture, proportion, rhythmic motion, tone, etc. or by behavior or attitude, etc. A very attractive feature."*

Webster

– *"That which gives the highest degree of pleasure to the senses or to the mind and suggests that the object of delight approximates one's conception of an ideal."*

Webster

– *"That quality or combination of qualities which affords keen pleasure to the senses especially that of sight or which charms the intellectual or moral facilities."*

Shorter Oxford

$$\text{"} \quad \frac{\sqrt{5}+1}{2} = 1.618 \quad \text{"}$$

Have you ever thought about how much time and effort our society expends on the chance to experience or have a glimpse of beauty? We take vacations to see beautiful scenery and historical architecture. We acquire art, beautiful homes located in beautiful settings, and fancy automobiles. We buy designer clothes, shoes, jewelry, and we seek out the best cosmetologist for hair, make-up, and personal grooming. Many of us even exercise and diet to help in our effort to become beautiful, and finally, when all else fails, some of us go to

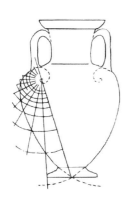

The beauty of a potter's vase and phi.

church for help in transforming our interior so that we can become beautiful people from the inside out!

Everyone seems to have an interest in beauty one way or another and through the ages society has spared no expense in its quest to create and build the ultimate in beauty. Nature has helped us in our quest to experience beauty by giving us perhaps the most beautiful of all her creations, the flower. All of us recognize the beauty of these masterpieces and we almost always use the flower to enhance special events or occasions in our lives. H.E. Huntley writes:

"Man by nature is a creator. After the likeness of his maker, man is born to create, to fashion beauty."

As most of us will agree, one of the most wonderful experiences available to man is that of creative activity. Ask the artist, the composer of music, the husband and wife, or even the mathematician. All of us love to create and it is obvious that all of us love beauty. Even the non-creative person is forever searching for beautiful objects created by the more talented. This search is carried out so that he may appreciate and enjoy the beautiful creations of another.

The Line of Beauty and the Golden Spiral.

The "Line of Beauty" or Hogarth Curve is the lazy S curve formed from a woman's shoulders down to her hips. Note the similar line in the growth pattern of the cascading bougainvillea and the beautiful spiral of the chaise bench. These lines correspond closely to the Golden Spiral and phi.

The Parabolic Curve symbolizing the beauty of the rainbow.   *J. Johnson*

Decorative Parabolic Curve

Parabolic curves found in man-made objects as diverse as the boomerang, suspension bridge supports, and the St. Louis arch have unbreakable strength. They are thrilling to look at and contemplate because the viewer can *feel* the tensile strength! This is *so* in floral design – one wonders why these two vases are not pushed apart by the "spring" in the flower stems. Therefore, this "design of the future" will leave its imprint on one's memory. This concept is dynamite! This particular design looks romantic due to the selection of materials which complement the handblown glass cornucopias – each flowing from its golden spiral starting point. The new appreciation of space within design cannot be more beautifully expressed than with the enclosed space of a parabolic curve.

Phi is expressed in overall proportion and materials:

Golden Rectangle:
    Height = 5
    Length = 8
Golden Spiral:
    Container = Φ
    Calla = Φ

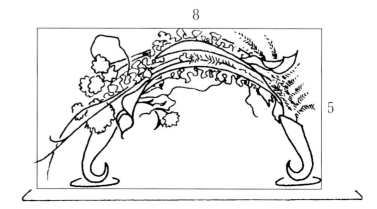

Consider this statement of J. Bronowski: *"In the moment of appreciation we live again the moment when the creator saw and held the hidden likeness.... We re-enact the creative act and we ourselves make the discovery again!"*

In his book <u>The Education of the Whole Man</u>, L.P. Jacks indicates that this love of beauty is the "driving power" which brings out the creative element in man and is "innate in everybody but is suppressed, smothered, thwarted in most of us...."

H.E. Huntley, in his book <u>The Divine Proportion</u>, indicates that there are two requirements for aesthetic appreciation: The first is given and the second is acquired. The first is from nature by inheritance and the second is from nurture by education. In other words, much of what we consider beautiful is inborn, the rest is learned. For example: we all love and appreciate the beauty of a rainbow, but the physicist's level of appreciation is much deeper because of what he knows and understands about the laws of physics taking place to bring us this beautiful creation of nature.

In my search for design, I have been intrigued most by what I believe is our inborn concept of the aesthetic appreciation of beauty. We all seem to very closely agree about what we think is beautiful. This agreement on beauty explains valuable art, favorite architecture, and beautiful scenery around the world that all of us enjoy. As you might guess, of course, phi is usually present in all of the best of these beautiful creations.

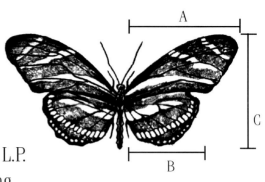

$$\frac{A}{B} = \Phi$$

$$\frac{C}{\text{Body length}} = \Phi$$

(55)
Phi and the butterfly.

A tribute to my beautiful mother, Dimple Jean Harwell.

"Man by nature is a creator after the likeness of the maker."
H.E. Huntley

43

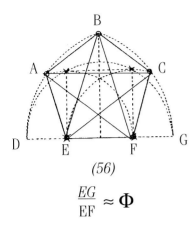

(56)

$$\frac{EG}{EF} \approx \Phi$$

Pentagram, Star, Gothic and Phi

(57)

ARCHITECTURE

The Parthenon, as previously noted, is considered one of the most beautiful monuments ever constructed, and it is full of golden rectangles. Most of us do not understand its construction architecturally, but we all instinctively appreciate its beauty.

Consider the grandeur of the pyramids in which the golden section and Fibonacci progression of 55, 89, 144 are believed to have been used in engineering their construction. This calculation, called the squaring of the circle, was also used in building Stonehenge and all who have seen these structures applaud their beauty and magnificence.

In addition to Egyptian and Greek architecture, phi and the golden ratio are found to be important in Roman and Gothic architecture. These beautiful works of art with their majestic Gothic curves are based on the five-pointed star *(Illus. 56)* which is heavily involved with the golden section. This use of the golden section and Φ contributed greatly to the construction of Chartres Cathedral in France *(Illus. 57)* which had the largest Gothic span completed up to that date. It is not known how the builders calculated it or how they thought it would ever stand up, but it has not shifted in seven hundred years! Perhaps the golden proportion translates into structural strength as well as beauty and balance.

Another beautiful cathedral which relies heavily on the golden section is the Cathedral of Notre Dame *(Illus. 58)*. The front entrance is a series of golden rectangles and its Gothic interior is full of phi. Many Persian mosques and Asian temples are also detailed according to the golden section of which the Taj Mahal *(Illus. 59)*, one of the seven wonders of the modern world, is a beautiful example.

More recently, architect Frank Lloyd Wright is believed to have been inspired by this proportion as are many of the most versatile architects of today. Phi and the golden section is still an important tool of proportion for these architects as shown in the work of Le Corbusier and his development of the modular concept, which uses the golden section as a comprehensive system of proportions. His work has played an important part in bringing the golden section into twentieth-century architecture. These and many other examples of classic architecture have withstood the test of time both

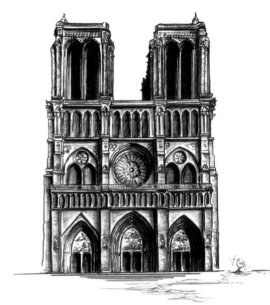

(58)

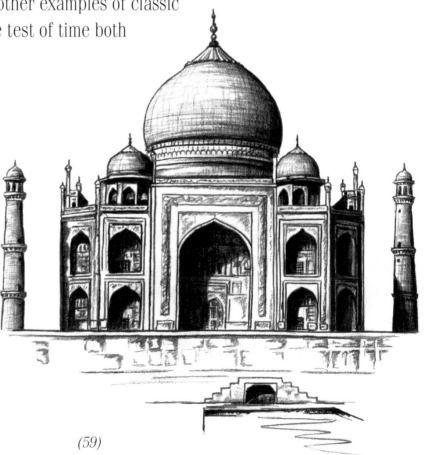

(59)

(60)

structurally and aesthetically. We would never think of implosion when we look upon these masterpieces. H.E. Huntley has suggested that a person gets a greater sense of abandonment when he sees a modern high-rise building than when he experiences a beautiful cathedral. This thought is further supported by the following quote by Keith Critchlow:

> *"Whenever a person enters an interior space he more or less becomes part of that space. Most people experience this whatever their interest, be it tourist or pilgrim....*
>
> *The beautiful cathedral nourishes the fundamental hope that our material existence is not all there is....*
>
> *If a building enlightens one person every two hundred years, it has done its job...."*
>
> Keith Critchlow

> *"A beautifully constructed work of architecture has been called a symphony of petrified or frozen music."*
>
> Plato

(61)

ART

Most interest in the golden section through the ages has been centered around art. Many of our greatest artists used this ratio when creating some of the most treasured masterpieces. Leonardo De Vinci was very much aware of phi and used it in his most famous piece, The Mona Lisa *(Illus.61)*. Also, his Virgin and Child with St. Anne is a composition using the golden section. The paintings of Botticelli, Hals, and Turner all display the beautiful ratio of phi. In his Madonna with Child and Two Angels, Botticelli made use of the golden section in the composition by placing divine subjects in the golden section focal point which gives a natural structural focus on the subject.

George Seurat's oil, <u>La Parade</u> *(Illus. 62)*, is composed of ovals and rectangles arranged in an overall pattern based on the golden mean system. Seurat may be one of those artists who temporarily rediscovered the golden section as many artists have from time to time. In fact, the golden section was his "master trump or secret trick." Many of his last works were "harmonically subdivided with the golden section." More recently Grant Wood's painting, <u>The American Gothic</u> *(Illus. 63)*, when analyzed, reveals that the golden section was the foundation for the structure.

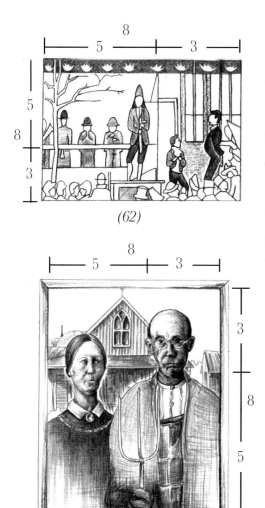

(62)

"Love of beauty is taste –
The creation of beauty is art."
Ralph Waldo Emerson

(63)

(64)
Mondrian's use of the Golden Rectangle is self-evident in <u>*Composition in Red, Yellow, and Blue*</u>*, 1921.*

(65)

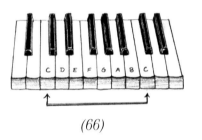

(66)

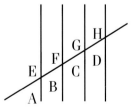

*All corresponding angles
are equal*
∠ A = ∠ B = ∠ C = ∠ D
∠ E = ∠ F = ∠ G = ∠ H

(67)

MUSIC

It would be impossible to have a complete discussion of beauty without a discussion of music. One of the most famous and best composers, Mozart, used phi and the golden section in the composition of his <u>Symphony in G Minor</u> as a temporal expression. Many other musicians since Mozart have also used nature's ratio of beauty to enhance their music and make it more interesting. The major sixth, which is the chord that our ears like the best, vibrates very close to phi in the ratio of the notes E to C. These notes produce good vibrations in the cochlea of our ear, which is itself shaped in the form of nature's golden spiral *(Illus. 65)*. It is also interesting to observe that there are 8 white keys and 5 black keys in an octave on the piano *(Illus. 66)*, which are both Fibonacci numbers. Even recent works in dance and choreography have shown an interest in Fibonacci and phi.

MATHEMATICS

A final discussion involving beauty will cover the subject of mathematics. Is there beauty in mathematics? Perhaps there is! H.W. Huntley, author and mathematician, observed Peter Fraser, Lecturer in Mathematics:

"Professor Peter Frazier fanned four vertical lines on the blackboard, crossed them with a transversal, and wrote an equation. He then made the following comment, while waving his arms enthusiastically and speaking in staccato: 'Oh, a truly beautiful theorem! Beautiful! Beautiful! Look at it! Look at it! What simplicity! What economy! Just four lines and one transversal.' His voice rises to a crescendo.

'Its generality is astonishing.' Then muttering to

himself, 'beautiful!...beautiful!...' He stopped, slightly embarrassed, and returned to earth."

It is virtually impossible to overemphasize the importance of phi and the Fibonacci number sequence and their relevance to the mathematical and physical sciences. These numbers appear in almost every branch of mathematics: number theory, differential equations, probability statistics, numerical analysis, and linear algebra. They even occur in physics, biology, chemistry, electrical engineering, and as we have already pointed out, in nature and all the arts. Almost everything that we consider beautiful seems to be involved with this simple mathematical ratio! Is there beauty in mathematics?

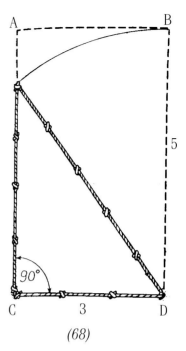

(68)

Golden Rectangle and 3 - 4 - 5 Triangle

$$\frac{BD}{CD} = \Phi$$

$$\Phi = \frac{\sqrt{5}+1}{2} = 1.618 = BEAUTY$$

"The hours when we are absorbed by beauty are the only hours when we really live....

These are the only hours that absorb the soul and fill it with beauty. This is real life, and all else is illusion, or mere endurance."

Richard Jefferies

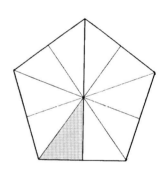

3 - 4 - 5 Triangle, Pentagon and phi.

"He has made everything beautiful in its time. He has also set eternity in the heart of men; yet they cannot fathom what God has done from beginning to end."

Ecclesiastes *3:11*

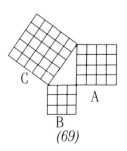

(69)

Pythagoreum Theorum

$$A^2 + B^2 = C^2$$

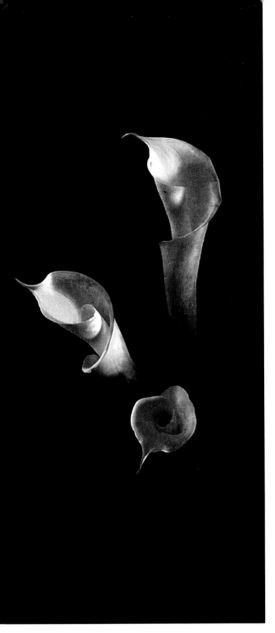

CHAPTER V
Fibonacci, Fibonacci...
Is There More?

How many other things does nature's mathematical ratio of phi influence in our lives? I would not suggest that anything more than has already been discussed is necessary to convince anyone of the importance of this ratio as it relates to design. I do, however, want all who read about this adventure to see the complete picture revealed to me during my search for design.

One of the most interesting influences that phi has on each of us is in our field of vision. The human visual limit is very close to the golden rectangle and the field of color vision is almost exactly equal to phi. (Field of color vision includes the dimensions of the field where we see color). Perhaps this is one of the reasons the dimensions of phi look right and feel right to most of us.

Discovering the fact that our visual limitations were related to phi was not as surprising to me as the possibility of a phi and Fibonacci relationship to the stock market, taxation, psychology, computers, fiber-optics and astro-physics.

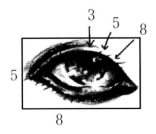

(70)
W = 8 H = 5 = Golden Rectangle

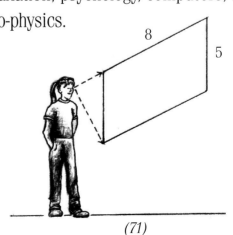

(71)

If anyone had told me that there was any order to the stock market or taxation, I would have had serious doubts until I read a couple of articles relating stock market retracements and taxation to Fibonacci and the golden mean. Many brokers use 38.2% and 61.8% or phi to compute retracement levels (a pause or reverse trend), of a previous stock move. Phi also shows up as a guide for taxation. It has been suggested that any tax above a critical point very close to the golden mean, 38.2%, would retard economic activity and bring in less, rather than more, tax revenue.

Psychologists also have done their share of research into the 61.8%/38.2% golden ratio. Normal social behavior shows that out of 100 introductions to new people or other events in the world that 61.8% of the responses will be positive and 38.2% will be negative. Perhaps we all need a certain percentage of negative stimuli to make the positive meaningful. Too much of a good thing may not always be the best for us, and maybe the golden ratio and phi does have significance psychologically, therefore, even influencing our feelings about design. Psychological research relating to the golden section and phi is very involved and technical, but the results support the relevance of the 61.8/38.2 phi proportion.

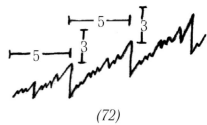

(72)
The stockmarket and phi.

(73)
Taxation and phi.

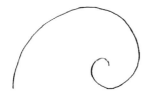

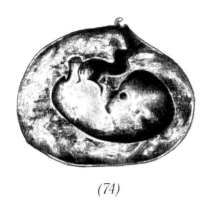

(74)

Computers, fiber-optics, and astrophysics have also found an interest in Fibonacci and phi in programming, creating order, and finding random numbers. Even the developing fetus in the womb shows the golden spiral at work *(Illus. 74)*. Also, the golfer utilizes this amazing spiral as he perfects his golf swing *(Illus. 75)*. The list could go on, but I think one can see the significant role that the beautiful ratio of Phi plays in each of our lives.

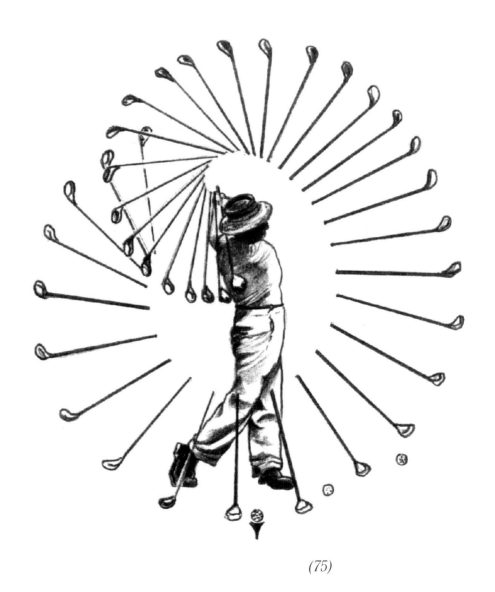

(75)

(76)

The lion's claw is an impressive example of the Golden Spiral.

Note the balance and beauty of his face: nose (3), mouth (5), eyes (8).

(77)

CHAPTER VI
Thoughts on Creation

*...a sense of awe and fear caused my
thought process to stop and turn away...*

This observation is part of a statement that I
wrote after becoming aware of Luca Pacioli's book, Di
Devina Proportione (1500). Through his insights and
evaluation of phi and the golden section, Pacioli came up
with the following analogies as detailed by Charles
Bouleau:

The golden section...

– *"Like God, it is unique."*

– *"As the Holy Trinity is one substance in
three persons, it is one single proportion in three
terms."*

– *"As God cannot be described in words, it
cannot be expressed by any intelligible number or
rational quantity but is always secret and is called
by the mathematician, irrational."*

– *"Like God, it is always similar to itself."*

These statements created a lot of interest and
intrigue in my thought process, but I was very skeptical.
How could this simple ratio of phi have such a significant
impact. As I continued meditating on Pacioli's insights,

an interesting thought came to me that eased some of my skepticism. No creation reflected phi and the golden ratio as radiantly as man – especially the balance and proportion of his face, but also his entire body from the tip of his finger to his toe. And then, I had another thought!

> Then God said, "Let us make man in our image after our likeness".
> Genesis *1:26*

My heart started racing and a sense of awe and fear caused my thought process to stop and turn away. My search for design had just given me a mental glimpse of the physical reality of our creator. After asking myself if I had the courage to continue, I slowly began putting the pieces together, and for the first time I could see visual evidence of the omniscience, omnipotence and omnipresence of God. To my delight, I finally understood visually and intellectually the order, balance, and beauty of all creation, both in our world and through the entire universe. Although my search for design will never end, I no longer have to ask why. The fundamental design principle and formula for beauty has been made clear and evident through the ratio of phi. Any artist can use this evidence as a springboard for the creative designs of tomorrow.

H.E. Huntley suggests that man by nature is a creator and after the likeness of his maker, man was born to be creative. Plato, in his book Timaeus said "*...and it was then that all these kinds of things thus established received their shapes from the ordering one, through the action of ideas and numbers...*"

The fact that phi and the golden ratio is revealed from the atom to the galaxies and from DNA to the overall structure of man and nature is strong evidence supporting the importance of this simple beautiful ratio throughout our world and universe. Perhaps it is even strong enough to support Pacioli's idea of "The Divine Proportion."

"Ever since the creation of the world his invisible nature, namely, his eternal power and deity, has been clearly perceived in the things that have been made."

Romans *1:20*

"God saw all that he had made, and it was very good."

Genesis *1:31*

MAGNIFICENT! WONDERFUL! BEAUTIFUL!
Simply beautiful... beautiful....

CHAPTER VII

Phi & Floral Design

Fibonacci's 3-5-8, Phi and Floral Design

"A great designer does not design because it is useful, but because he delights in it!"
H. E. Huntley

Some people have an instinct for good proportion and creating beautiful designs. Whatever they plan or design seems always to please the eye. This is not the case for most people however. Those of us who do not have the instinct must study to aquire this trait, and fortunately it is one that can be aquired.

The golden rectangle of Greek Architecture is believed by some artists to have perfect proportion and to have been used in the construction of the Parthenon, known as the most perfectly proportioned building in the world. The ratio of the height to the width of the Greek's golden rectangle is equal to phi or 1.618. Although the ratios involved in the design concept of 3-5-8 are not exactly equal to 1.618 (5/3 = 1.66 8/5 = 1.60), they are close enough and look good to the human eye. Gregor Lersch, in one of his design lectures, made an interesting point in saying that when a design style is selected and the proportions are laid out, the designer may "fiddle with the edges" as long as the style maintains its integrity. In other words, the 3-5-8 of design is not an exact science but a guideline to achieve design excellence and beauty. Even the guideline of making a design 1.5 times the height of the container or three times to add more drama is a simple way of saying the container is (3), the floral content is (5), and the overall subject is (8). Almost all aspects of good design are directly or indirectly affected by phi and 3-5-8.

To understand how the 3-5-8 of Fibonacci and Nature's ratio of phi relates to Floral Design it will be necessary to explain and demonstrate their influence on the "elements and principles" of design. This explanation will include a definition and interesting characteristics of each "element and principle", as well as a photo demonstration and pencil illustration.

According to Helen Evans in <u>Man the Designer</u>, the concepts that constitute the language of design are its "elements and principles." Understanding them allows us to communicate with one another about design. The elements of design have been described by Ms. Evans as the visual components used by the designer or artist to create a composition of art. The designer may use some or all of these design elements when creating. The elements of design include line, form, space, color, and texture.

The principles of design are the way in which elements are combined or organized by the designer to bring unity to the creation. These principles include proportion, balance, rhythm, focal point/area, and harmony. The complimentary functioning of each element determines the success with which the designer will have in applying the principles to his design.

Jim Johnson, AIFD, in a recent program "Blueprints of Style", lists line, form, space, color, and texture, as the elements of design; and proportion, balance, focal point, rhythm, and harmony as principles of floral design. Our discussion will center around these ten elements and principles.

Elements of Design

Line, Form, Space, Color, and Texture

Line:

Line is probably the most significant and easiest element of design for us to understand because everything around us has line. Examples of line would be vertical, horizontal, slanting, zig zag, circular, spiral, and curving. Line in print (books and newspapers) allows us to communicate and also extends and supplements our lives through education. The importance of line for floral designers cannot be overemphasized because it can be instrumental in determining the personality and feeling of the design. For example:

Strong vertical - suggests majesty, dignity, and formality

Horizontal - suggests approachable or informal

Diagonal - (like bending boughs in a storm) produces psychic tension, very dynamic with a feeling of activity

Spiral - suggests infinity like vines and sea shells

Zig Zag - suggests excitement like lightning

Actively curved - suggests feelings of restlessness and agitation

Moderately curved - suggests restful and graceful

The manner in which line is used in a design determines not only the style of the arrangement but also its proportion and balance. Fibonacci's 3-5-8 of design when applied to line will give a more pleasing proportion and in turn create balance. Many times strong vertical lines are reinforced by repetition using 2's, 3's, or 5's–all Fibonacci numbers.

Abstract Design

In an abstract design, the plant material may either lose its identity, or its identity becomes secondary to its function as a form or color. In this design, the blue ting ting becomes a rectangular mass against which the orange curly willow branch becomes an erratic line of electric energy. The contrast is complete in both form and color. The eye finds this dominant line to be magnetic.

Phi is obvious in the overall dimensions:

Depth (front to back) = 3
Width = 5
Height = 8

And in the orange line:

Lower section = 3
Upper section = 5
Total = 8

And textures:

Ceramic = 3
Willow = 5
Ting Ting = 8

Balance, Proportion, Line, Rhythm, and Texture are self-evident in this composition.

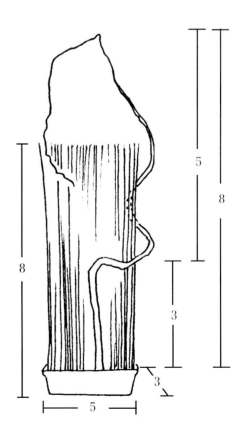

J. Johnson

orm:

Form can be described as the area, mass, or shape of a design. Man seems always to have had a concern with form as is demonstrated by architecture through the ages. The pyramids of Egypt and the castles of Europe are examples. Tall vertical form has expression toward the heavenly, with elegance, stateliness, and dignity. Low form expresses closeness with nature or earthly life.

The most familiar forms used in floral design are geometric: triangles, ovals and circles. Some other forms would include composites such as trapezoids, pentagons, hexagons, octagons and stars. Less rigid and organic forms are the ellipse and the parabola.

The components within the design also contribute to form. The proportions of the different types of form in the design add interest and create beauty and most of the time, these proportions relate to Fibonacci numbers and the beautiful ratio of phi.

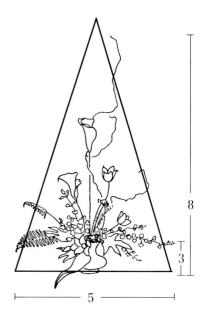

Decorative "Everyday" Design

The simple everyday design that is mass-produced in many shops will look elegant – even majestic when its elements conform to phi! This one could never go out of style.

Phi is expressed through color:
> White = 3
> Green = 5
> Yellow = 8

And form:
> Mass materials (tulips) = 3
> Form materials (calla) = 5
> Filler materials
> (orchids,etc.) = 8
> Geometric Form = Golden
> Triangle:
> Base = 5
> Height = 8

And proportion:
> Design depth = 3
> Design width = 5
> Total height = 8

And textures:
> Velvety = 3
> Waxy = 5
> Frilly = 8

Golden spiral = callas = Φ

K. McConnico

$\mathcal{Space}$:

Space is the element of design that primarily refers to open areas around individual flowers and foliage in the arrangement. The ratio of phi and Fibonacci can be demonstrated utilizing space to make a design more interesting and therefore more aesthetically pleasing. The quantity of open space to closed space and the interval between them will be more interesting and beautiful if Fibonacci and phi are used.

Formal Linear Design

The forms and lines in this design are accentuated by spaces - some of which are enclosed - that surround them. Great energy is produced by the tension seen in every curve. The eye is drawn upward through each bend until it reaches the top, and then it is directed back down - to recirculate. Color interest is brought out because the smallest volume of color, **white**, completely overpowers the largest volume, **brown**.

Phi can be seen in:
 Height of base = 3
 Width of design = 5
 Height of design = 8
And in the ratio of colors:
 White = 3
 Green = 5
 Brown = 8
The use of space:
 Upper area = 3
 Lower area = 5

<u>Line</u>, the most evident element directs the eye and at the same time emphasizes the <u>focal</u> <u>area</u> because of its <u>color</u>. In addition, the use of the framing technique calls attention to the calla lily. Repetition of forms produces <u>rhythm</u>, and contrasting textures create <u>interest.</u>

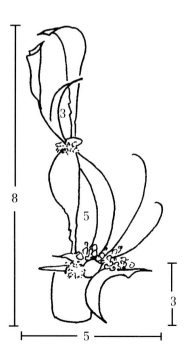

K. McConnico

Color:

Color is the name given to the reflections of visual wave lengths from surfaces. When all of a prism's wave lengths are reflected, the color is white, or with no waves reflected – black. If a surface absorbs all waves but green, the surface is green.

Color is an element that has the most potential in stimulating a response or arousing emotion in relation to a design. Suggestions have been made which tie certain colors to particular feelings, such as red with blood, life, and vibrancy; blue with cool; purple with rage; pink with embarrassment.

Research has proven that it is usually more satisfying to have one color predominant rather than having colors in equal portions. This suggests that the 3-5-8 of Fibonacci or the phi ratio could apply. When applying Fibonacci and phi to the use of color, one might use an analogous scheme: the predominant color (8) would be a light tint; medium color (5) would be next in prominence; with the deep rich color (3) being the least amount of color used.

A small amount of light color (3) or (5) will balance a large quantity (8) of dark. Also, a small amount of intense color (3) or (5) will balance a larger amount of neutral color (8). Color can also be balanced in a design by using a smaller portion of its complement by placing it in the center of the design or by repeating it in various areas. For example, a predominantly blue (8) green (5) arrangement may have a thrust of red (3) to balance the colors.

The most beautiful color schemes are those which give a single impression of warmth with a note of coolness for variation or coolness with an accent of warmth.

J. Johnson

Interpretive Round Design

A Biedermier pie! Concentric rings
are arranged in a ceramic "deep dish" pie plate.
This pastry cooks up phi in a number of ways:
    In color values:

        Pure chroma (roses) = 3
        Pastel values
            (stock, grapes) = 5
        Dark values (pansy, aster
                stock) = 8

And in textures:
    Inner circles -
        Frilly (stock) = 3
        Smooth (roses) = 5
        Bristley (asters) = 8
    Outer circles -
        Smooth (grapes) = 3
        Frilly (stock) = 5
        Velvety (pansy) = 8

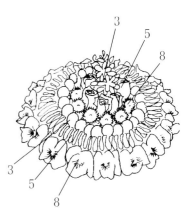

$\mathcal{T}$exture:

Texture is an element of design that has both physical and visual qualities and it may be sensed by touch or sight. Some examples of texture are rough, smooth, soft, hard, wet, slick, velvet, new, old, dull and shiny.

Fibonacci's 3-5-8 works again when selecting materials to go into a design for interest, balance and aesthetic beauty: for example, the phi proportion of rough to smooths or the very rough (3), medium (5), and smooths (8).

Vegetative Landscape Design

This beautiful rugged design immediately captures interest because of the dramatic variation in the texture of the materials used. The phi relationship between these materials works again in creating interest.

Proportion:

Width to Height = Φ

Texture:

Fuzzy = 3
Smooth = 5
Rough = 8

O. Honjo

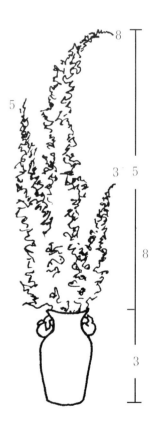

Ikebana — Ikenabo Shoka Style

The utter simplicity of native juniper compliments an exquisitely detailed Oriental vase.

Phi is expressed in the three lines:

Shin = 8   (heaven)
Soe = 5   (man)
Tai = 3   (earth)

B.Bigham

Principles of Design

Proportion, Balance,
Focal Point/Area, Rhythm, and Harmony

The principles of design are utilized when an artist organizes or arranges the design elements; i.e., Line, Form, Space, Texture, and Color. According to Helen Marie Evans in her book, <u>Man the Designer</u>, this organization of the elements using the design principles brings a meaningful relationship between each of the elements. Jim Johnson, Professor of Floral Design at Texas A&M University, has stated that these design principles are "fundamental guidelines that help the designer achieve excellence in composition." Interestingly enough, as you might guess, nature's ratio of phi or Fibonacci is usually involved in the most beautiful and pleasing of these designs.

Some designers seem to have a natural instinct for the organization of design qualities or elements and again they all seem to coincide with phi and Fibonacci.

"The Greeks established classic proportion over 2,000 years ago, and it is as valid now as it was then. If basic principles are ignored, arbitrary design results.... New materials are being developed with possibilities of performance and workability that are dangerously exciting to the designer's imagination. Unless we thoroughly understand **how these** *materials can work for us, and above all, how a finished product will work for the consumer and with other products he will use, then we will fail to create excellence in design."*

David Infield Wilson

$\mathcal{Proportion}$

Proportion is the one principle which has a close relationship to all of the elements and principles of design. Proportion is the mathematical ratio or the quantitative comparisons of form or material used in one part of a design to those of another part. These ratios would apply to line (length, width, and height). Form (the size of small forms in in relation to larger, or round compared to square). Space (quantity of open space compared to closed and their intervals). Texture (the amount of smooth surface compared to rough), and Color (amount of rust compared to the amount of blue). Proportion also determines balance, dictates rhythm, and produces harmony. It is the mathematical fiber that ties the entire composition or design together to make it work and become a creation of beauty. It is interesting to note that if these proportions are close to Fibonacci's 3-5-8, or phi, they are usually more aesthetically pleasing to the human eye.

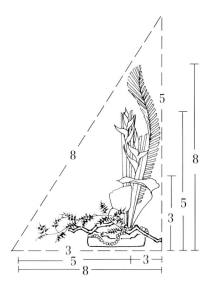

Formal Linear

This design features dramatic combination of forms and lines, each having enough space to show itself off. The complementary color harmony of red and green increases the drama.

Phi is expressed through color:
  Light green = 3
  Red = 5
  Dark green = 8
Or if the container is included:
  Gray = 3
  Red = 5
  All greens = 8
And it is shown in two ways through proportion:
Width:
  Right of focal point = 3
  Left of focal point = 5
  Total width = 8
Height:
  Top of 2 anthurium
      leaves = 3
  Top of red heleconias = 5
  Total height = 8

Line is expressed dramatically in the clipped areca palm leaf which also moves the eye in a spiral toward the center. Additional lines are more relaxed, but very interesting in their erratic horizontal presentation through the curly willow branch, *Asparagus plumosis* and the strand of brussel sprouts. Open spaces are usually detrimental to a focal point, but in this design, two very striking leaves frame the focal area actually calling attention to the exact place where the forceful heleconias and other stems emerge, thus creating a feeling of stability and at the same time emphasizing the brussel sprouts. Balance is asymmetrical. Textures repeat themselves, giving a strong feeling of rhythm to the design.

J. Johnson

Balance

Helen Evans has stated that balance is so closely related to proportion that it is difficult to evaluate a design without referring to them both. Proper proportion develops and reinforces balance and creates a sensation of equilibrium and feeling of stability.

Again Fibonacci and phi are usually found in both symmetrical and asymmetrical balance. In most pleasing symmetrical forms one will find phi when dividing the composition in half. In asymmetrical design 3-5-8 proportion is the most used to create balance and beauty.

O. Honjo

Horizontal Formal Linear

What an excellent example of dramatic asymmetrical balance as the eye moves from the heaviness of the intensely colored sunflower along the slender Trumpet Vine! It is reminiscent of a grammar school teeter-totter with two children close to the fulcrum on one side and a much lighter single child at the farthest extreme at the other end of the board. Phi and the teeter-totter are a perfect example of how to acheive balance in floral design.

Proportion:

        Depth =3   Stand = 3
        Height = 5   Arrangement Height = 5
        Width = 8   Arrangement Width = 8

Form:

        Triangular 3-5-8

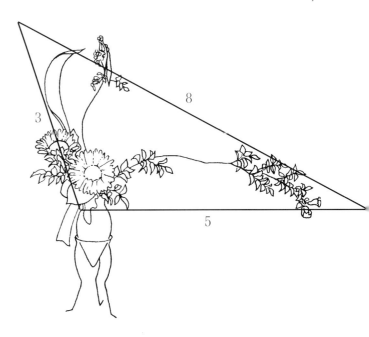

Focal Point/Area

Focal point is the principle of design that carries the eye to the most important area of the arrangement. Before deciding on a focal point the designer must decide (1) what to emphasize (2) how to emphasize (3) how much to emphasize and (4) where to place the emphasis. The focal point should also be simple, beautiful, and suitable to the design purpose. Fibonacci and phi can play an important part in drawing attention and attracting the eye to the focal area.

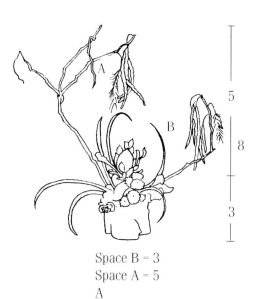

Space B = 3
Space A = 5
$$\frac{A}{B} = \Phi$$

Ikebana Moribana (Contrasting Style)

Everything about this composition places emphasis on the protea focal area. It is therefore not surprising that phi is involved not only in space but also proportion as the mesquite branches and foliage surround the protea.

Proportion:

Container = 3
Lower Branch = 5
Tall Branch = 8

Space:

Between Branches = Φ

O. Honjo

Rhythm

Rhythm has been described as the idea of a pleasing related movement; i.e., the beat of march music, a ballerina taking the stage in two, three, and five steps (all Fibonacci numbers), a leaking faucet, or a continuous line movement (Hogarth's "Line of Beauty", and flower petals forming radial rhythm). Rhythm can be attained through repetition of shapes, progression of sizes, easily connected or continuous line movement, and color placement. The related movement of rhythm in a design helps draw the eye through the design which creates interest and intrigue. Rhythm has even been described as the most sensuously appealing of all the principles since it involves our kinesthetic sense as well as our visual sense, which further explains rhythm's appeal. Fibonacci and phi can even play an important part in rhythm by using the 3-5-8 of line. Gregor Lersch in a recent lecture "sang" an example of rhythm in this manner:

Da - - - Da - - - - - - - - - - - - Da - - - - - - -
(An irregular spacing between each note)

This is much more interesting than:

Da - - - Da - - - Da - - -
(An equal spacing between each note)

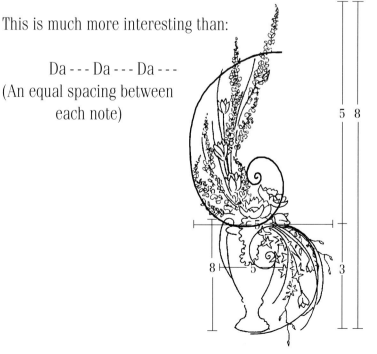

Decorative Hogarth Curve

This composition presents flowers in the contrived, but traditional "S" curve - what William Hogarth, the renown English engraver called the "line of beauty." It requires a tall container or a pedestal so the lower segment can cascade downward without any restriction. The pleasing beauty of this elegant design is due to phi. Both vase and design express Phi in their dimensions in height and width:

Proportion:
Depth = 3
Width = 5
Height = 8
or:
The lower curve = 3
The upper curve = 5
Overall = 8
The vase:
The foot = 3
The bowl (in width) = 5
The total height = 8
This design expresses color relationships in phi also:
Shades = 3
Pastels = 5
Medium hues = 8

Golden spiral is revealed in upper and lower curve and in the lines of the container.

Line is created by a progression of flower forms (tulips, snapdragons, dendrobium orchids) out of the focal point. It is enhanced by long smooth foliages. Repetition of these forms and lines produces rhythm. The focal area is created with the open peonies floating on the clusters of grapes. Asymmetrical balance extends to either side of the central axis in different quantities and helps develop the proportion.

J. Johnson

Harmony

Harmony is the principle of design that produces an impression of unity through the selection and arrangement of containers, flowers, foliages, and other materials. To have harmony each of these components must be friendly and have kinship to one another.

Combining warm colors with warm, and cool colors with cool also creates harmony. The proportion of these colors will be more interesting and beautiful if Fibonacci's 3-5-8 is applied.

Vegetative Design

Harmony is evident in this composition as one observes the wild flowers and grasses as if they were growing along the West Texas roadside on a mid-summer day. The materials were selected because they do grow and bloom together in their natural habitat. The basket also blends harmoniously with the composition.

O. Honjo

Gallery of Designs

Jim Johnson, AIFD

Bob Bigham, AIFD

Osamu Honjo, AIFD

Gary Norman

Ken McConnico

Dan Harwell

Electric Energy, Phi, and the Creative Designer!

J. Johnson

Jim Johnson, AIFD

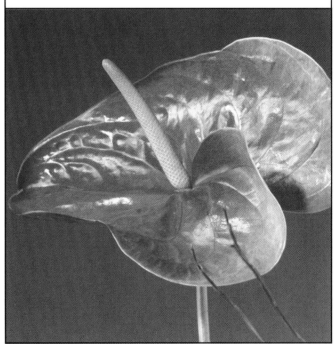

Decorative Traditional Design

The Flemish painting is a composition controlled by the artist. Flowers may be placed in the container side-by-side that could never grow or bloom side-by-side in the garden. One of each thing. Over dramatize with rich staging. Status symbol. Show off! Color and mood saturates the eye. The viewer would never see phi in this composition, but the artist employs the concept to create a 'perfect' composition.

The canvas is divided into *Dimensions* of height and width:

Container = 3
Tapestry = 5
Flowers = 8

Formal Linear Budvase

The simplest design may be analyzed according to the concept of phi.

In terms of volume, phi reveals:

Aspidistra leaf = 3

Vase = 5

Anthurium = 8

And color:

Dark = 3

Light = 5

Bright = 8

Golden Spiral:

Spath of Anthurium

Clear glass — especially *thick* clear glass — magnifies the mechanics. One does not want the stems to visually overpower the artistic vase of the beautiful flower. These stems were carefully wrapped with a single blade of a fan palm leaf. In this manner, the mechanics become a visually attractive part of the design!

Graphic Parabolic Curve

This interpretation of the parabolic curve does not let the viewer down – the energy that one *expects* to see bursting out of the arch does just that – in the form of the callas! Each willow is suffused with tension. The interlocking lines and spaces create a great deal of tension while the two aspidistra leaves offer relief to the eye. The singular orange provides focus and stability in an otherwise kinetic design.

Phi can be seen instantly in the ratio of colors and in materials:

Orange = 3
White = 5
Green and Brown = 8

And in the dimensions:

Depth = 3
Height = 5
Width = 8

Golden spiral: callas

Line and rhythm are very strong and the motion produced contributes to the feeling of asymmetrical balance.

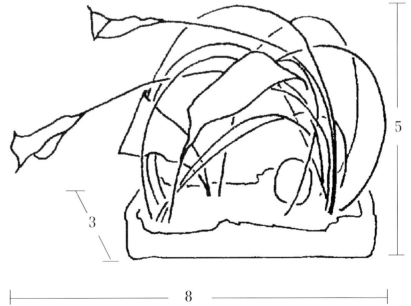

Parallel Vegetative Design

The concept of vegetative placement of materials in this design is stylized by the introduction of the parallel lines of the "singular" materials - irises, roses, ornithogalum and *Asparagus springeri meyerii*. The non-parallel materials huckleberry, curly willow and fillers serve to frame the garden and add natural vegetative interest at the base. The mushrooms and weathered wood create accents and develop a woodsy theme that harmonizes with the basket.

Phi is expressed in the proportions:
Width of container = 3
Height to tip of iris = 5
Total height = 8

Color:
Yellow = 3
White = 5
Green = 8

Texture, one of the strongest principles in this composition is illustrated through a great variety of surfaces. Balance is asymmetrical, Rhythm is apparent by repetition of textures, colors and forms, and Lines draw the eye both upward into the canopy and downward into the interesting base.

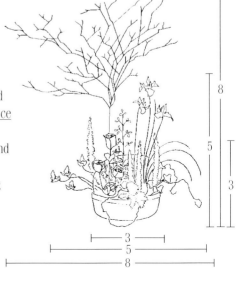

Abstract Design

"Out of Africa" is the name of this rather top-heavy "giraffe." The inverted root stalk of a *Philodendron selloum* simply arranged itself! The sunflower creates an all-seeing eye. Of course, this is pure imagination! What really matters is that the vegetative materials are used purely as forms and colors. This design proves that there is even a place for humor in floral design.

Again, phi shows up in nature's work:

Proportion:

Neck = 3
Head = 5
Body = 8

Color:

Yellow = 3
Green = 5
Brown = 8

Fibonacci & Spiral:

Sunflower petals and seeds

Texture is the dominant principle due to the obvious pattern of contrasting surface qualities. Line and rhythm lead the eye and produce feeling. Proportion makes the composition look comfortable, but seen as an animal representation, proportion makes the viewer smile. An interesting juxtaposition.

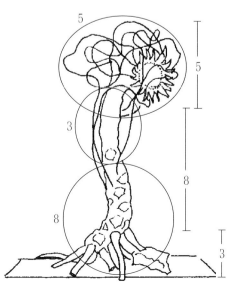

Equilateral Triangle Design

The standard American design is shown with attention-getting materials and color. Each flower is carefully placed and spaced giving the composition depth and creating interest and beauty. Phi can be found throughout in the various individual flower relationships through form, depth, color, and contrast.

Container = 3
Arrangement Depth = 5
Arrangement Height = 8

Color:

Orange Red = 3
Peach Rose = 5
Green and Blue = 8

Form:

Mass Foliage = 3
Small Flowers = 5
Bells of Ireland = 8

The application of Phi directs the placement of this design in its surroundings.

Podium

Altar

Foyer

Interpretive Geometric Design

In this solid rectangle framed in circles, tension is produced between the static body of larkspur and the energetic movement of willow. The framing technique of willow both encloses space and calls attention to the larkspur.

Phi is found in the volume:
Container = 3
Larkspur = 5
Willow = 8
And in color and texture:
Light brown/smooth = 3
Dark brown/rough = 5
Blue violet/soft = 8
Golden Rectangle:
Larkspur and Container = Φ

An interesting application of <u>balance</u> is found in how the asymmetrically placed willow provides a counterpoint to the solid symmetrical mass of larkspur. The staging of this composition illustrates how a base can provide emphasis – the wood grain visually extends the lines of willow.

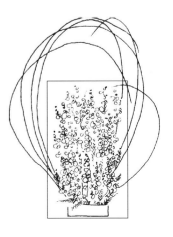

Bob Bigham, AIFD

Vegetative Landscape

Luxuriant growth is depicted in this truly opulent landscape. Each plant expresses tremendous vitality and energy. This energetic growth can almost be *felt*! Phi is expressed in three ways:

Proportion:

    Container = 3
    Right side = 5
    Left side = 8

Texture:

    Shiny/smooth = 3
    Coarse/hard = 5
    Soft/fuzzy = 8

Color:

    Red = 3
    Pink = 5
    Green = 8

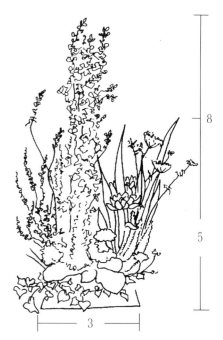

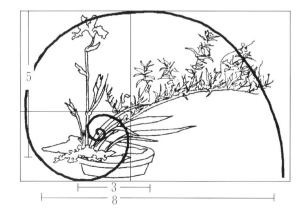

Ikebana Moribana Ikenebo Style

      Beautiful blooming desert willow reaches upward from the center of interest like a rainbow . . . another expression of phi:

      Bud development
            on Iris = 3 - 5 - 8
      Proportion:
            Container = 3
            Height of iris = 5
            Total width = 8
      Golden rectangle:
            Entire composition

Decorative — Hand-Tied Bouquet

The casual beauty of these flowers looks as if they fell into place without any conscious thought. Yet the artist has carefully grouped colors and textures for maximum impact. You can literally see the "violins, cellos and trumpets" in this pretty orchestration. Phi is consciously expressed through:

Color:

    White = 3
    Pastel pinks = 5
    Jewel tones = 8

And textures:

    Smooth = 3
    Rough = 5
    Fuzzy = 8

Proportion:

    Tied stems = 3
    Flowers and foliage = 5
    Overall = 8

5

3

Decorative Design

The artist has deftly used phi in the proportion of red to green. Nature does this automatically in producing variegated foliage by necessarily giving more area to chlorophyll-producing cells which sustain the plant – and less to the tissue which does not produce chlorophyll. In this composition, the nandina changing from green to red creates a logical transition color that harmonizes the two opposites and ties everything into the container. Phi is also found in:

Proportion:

Depth = 3 (front to back)
Height = 5
Width = 8

Formal Linear

This design is unique in that traditional materials only are incorporated into a formal linear format.

Phi is beautifully expressed through color:

Blue = 3
Green = 5
Red/Brown = 8

And container:

Foot = 3
Bowl = 5
Total = 8

And overall proportion:

Container height = 3
Design width = 5
Total height = 8

The principle of <u>rhythm</u> dominates this design because of repetition – repetition of curving lines (Scotch broom) and round forms (carnations). The use of broom to frame the iris creates <u>line</u> and forces the eye to circulate in a clockwise manner.

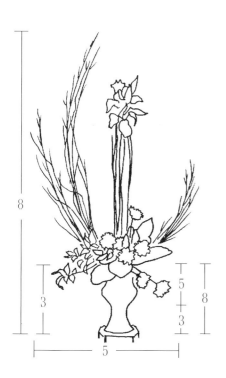

Decorative — Radial "Tuftwork"

This decorative composition is designed in the manner of a radial tuftwork with all stems directed into (or out of) the center. Each grouping of one type of plant material holds its individual identity within the composition.

Phi is expressed in the proportions:
Right side = 3
Height and left side = 5
Total width = 8

Asymmetrical <u>balance</u> is clearly visible; the <u>proportion</u> of flowers to container and contrasting <u>textures</u> make this design interesting and appealing. All stems direct the eye into the <u>focal point</u> of orange Gerberas.

Decorative Design — Hand-tied

Exquisitely delicate in color and texture and crowning a perfect golden spiral of handblown glass, this hand-tied bouquet expresses phi in several ways:

Color:

    Burgundy = 3
    Pink = 5
    White = 9

Texture:

    Smooth = 3
    Coarse = 5
    Frilly = 8

Flower Forms:

    Form (lily) = 3
    Mass (carnation) = 5
    Filler (Gypsophelia) = 8

Container = Golden Spiral = Φ

5

3

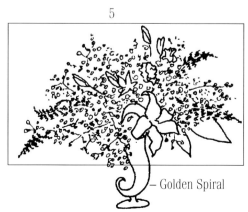

— Golden Spiral

Decorative "Tuftwork" Design

Tight groupings (tufts) of material emphasize each texture in this "family portrait". All stems draw the eye into the focal area. The radiating lines express phi in their length:

Gloxinia foliage = 3
Bells of Ireland = 5
Larkspur = 8

And color dispersion:

Blue (container) = 3
Violet = 5
Green = 8

The asymmetrical <u>balance</u> of this design is dynamic and the separation of textures makes each material more important.

Decorative Design

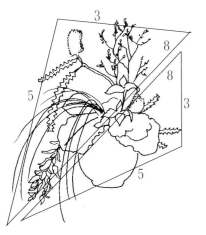

This composition of *bold* materials expresses the drama of contrasting textures. Each surface quality stands on its own, yet the overall presentation is stronger than its individual parts. Phi is expressed through both texture and proportion:

Texture:

Fuzzy = 3

Smooth = 5

Rough = 8

Proportion:

The mass is divided into two halves with the diagonal axis descending along the line of the longest material.

Apart from the principle of <u>texture</u>, <u>proportion</u> is beautifully expressed by combining *bold* materials with the *bold* container. Asymmetrical <u>balance</u> is achieved by extending the *Banksia protea* and olive to the left side and further emphasizing this directional flow by the placement of the large Ficus leaves.

Formal Linear — Interpretive

The horizontal orientation of lines and forms in this presentation frame the round container, thereby drawing attention to it. Rhythm is expressed through the repetition of line foliage and round flower clusters. Phi is found in:

Proportions:
>Depth = 3
>Height = 5
>Width = 8

Color:
>Green = 3
>Red = 5
>Bronze = 8

The Golden spiral is easily seen in the curl of the fern frond.

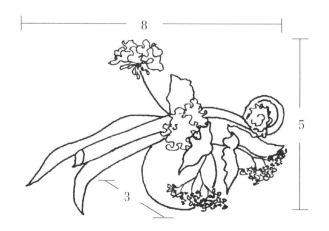

Formal Linear – Horizontal

This interesting composition displays teeter-totter fulcrum balance with the heavy protea and the slender graceful tulips. Phi is expressed in both weight and mass as illustrated:

Proportion:

Height of floral = 3
Height of container = 5
Overall = 8

Osamu Honjo, AIFD

Ikebana Nageire (Slanting Style)

What a wonderful combination of contrast between the rustic mountain cedar and the soft colorful Astilbe and Stargazer lillies. Phi is expressed in:

Volume:

Container = 3
Cedar Branch = 5
Flower Area =8

Form:

Astilbe = 3
Lilly = 5
Diffenbachia Foliage = 8

Ikebana Nageire (Cascading)

　　An elegant display of artistry emphasizing Ikebana in its style is created using materials from the desert and tropics. Phi is most evident in Form:

　　　　Lilly = 8
　　　　Spathiphyllum = 5
　　　　Small Foliage = 3
Texture:
　　　　Fuzzy to slick = Φ

Ikebana Nageire (Upright)

This stunning upright Ikebana design immediately captures one's interest as it reaches for the heavens. The feeling of balance and stability is contributed by phi.

Proportion:

Container = 3
Arrangement = 5
Overall = 8

Form:

The overall form of composition can accommodate the Golden Spiral.

The Golden Spiral can also be found in the anthurium spathe and the overall form.

8

3

5

Gary Norman

Ikebana

This Americanized contrasting style design is breathtaking in its simplicity! Color, texture and flower form find themselves in perfect <u>harmony</u> with each other and with the container. This free-form design could *fit* into an asymmetrical triangle, and this <u>space</u> relationship is repeated in the placement of roses. Phi is also found in <u>color</u> and <u>texture</u>:

    Yellow = 3
    Copper = 5
    Green = 8
  And volume:
    Roses = 3
    Container = 5
    Foliage = 8

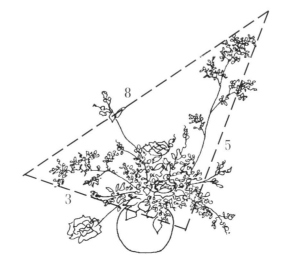

Decorative Topiary in Clay Pot

This traditionally "perfect" geometric form has been given a new sense of freedom. Tremendous rhythm (not a normal characteristic of topiaries) is expressed in the grapevine that frames the ball of flowers. The decorated pot at the base satisfies a need for the weight and volume that gives balance to the design. Pleasing proportion is due to phi.

Phi is seen in both the width and height ratios:

Width of trunk = 3
Width of decorated pot = 5
Width of ball = 8
Height of pot = 3
Height of pot and trunk = 5
Total height = 8
In color:
Deep red and violets = 3
Yellow = 5
Orange and terracotta = 8

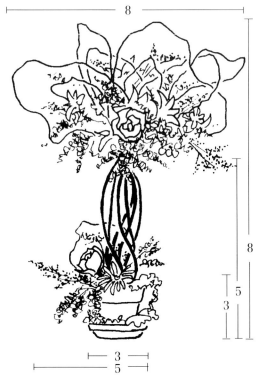

Decorative Topiary Display

For display purposes, three topiaries have been grouped in an obvious phi presentation. This technique adds impact and eye appeal to almost any kind of merchandise display.

Ken McConnico

Decorative Waterfall Design

The energy of water shooting over a precipice (callas) is tempered with "droplets" (seashells) falling gently downward in this romantic composition. The idea of water – or water fountain is seen instantly in the glass vase and its bubble counterpart. One can feel the flow of these multi-textured and layered materials.

This soft and delicate design never even suspects that it thrills the viewer! That is because it perfectly expresses the equation of phi: Golden Spiral is revealed in both descending crescents, seashells and callas.

$$\frac{A}{B} = 1.618 = phi$$

Rhythmic lines, contrasting textures, unexpected clear focal area, asymmetrical balance, and exquisite proportion together produce perfect harmony.

Decorative Crescent
(Traditional geometric design)

A crescent was created in this porcelain container because its sides flared upward and outward to the rim – as if it called for such a design.

The phi equation is responsible for this compositions appeal:

$$\frac{VOLUME\ 3}{VOLUME\ 2} = 1/618 = phi$$

And the volume of each section shows phi:

1 = 3
2 = 5
3 = 8

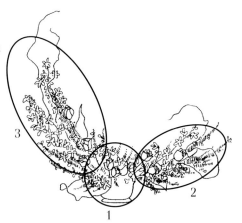

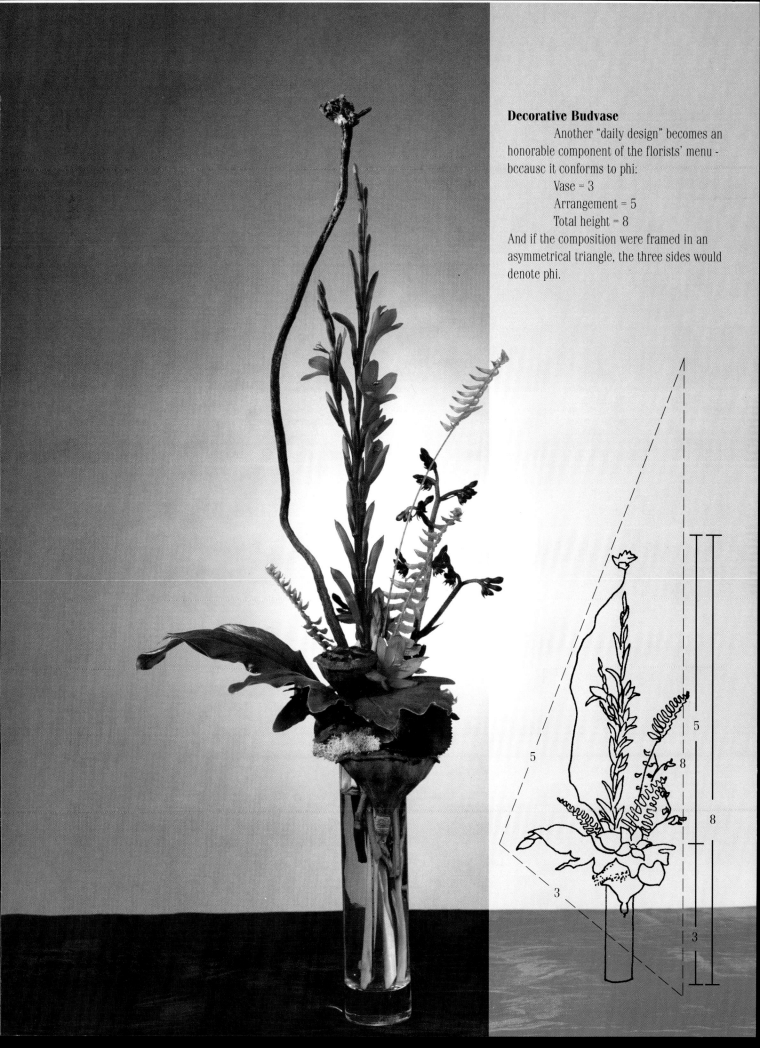

Decorative Budvase

Another "daily design" becomes an
honorable component of the florists' menu -
because it conforms to phi:

Vase = 3
Arrangement = 5
Total height = 8

And if the composition were framed in an
asymmetrical triangle, the three sides would
denote phi.

5

5

8

8

3

3

Dan Harwell

Graphic Vegetative Design

The vegetative placement of costus brings to mind a tropical desert isle. In fact, the gnarled wood could easily represent volcanic rock and the cones, boulders – a likely habitat for these tropical costus plants. The sunflower heads look as if they are floating in a tropical lagoon. Notice how the red blossoms repeat the form of the giant sugar cones. This composition is filled with golden spirals. Phi is found in the spiraling bracts of the costus and cones and in the seed pattern of the sunflowers. Phi can also be seen in the placement of cones:

       The left one = 3
       The right group = 5
       The center pair = 8

And in height:

       Wood and cone base = 3
       Right side = 5
       Left side = 8

And in the amounts of colors:

       Red = 3
       Green = 5
       Brown = 8

Golden Spiral:

       Pinecones
       Sunflowers
       Costus

The entire composition could fit into a golden rectangle with the base being delineated as a second rectangle. Look what happens when the spiral is superimposed - no wonder this composition is so pleasing to the eye!

Vegetative Desert Landscape
Phi is found:
Space = Φ
Spiraling spines
        on cactus = Φ
Rough to smooth = Φ

5

8

3

A

B

Space A = 3
Space B = 5
$\frac{B}{A}$ = Φ = 1.618...

Interpretive Geometric Design

This reproduction, in fresh flowers, of a mathematically correct golden rectangle is done to illustrate phi. It is made with the pavé technique.

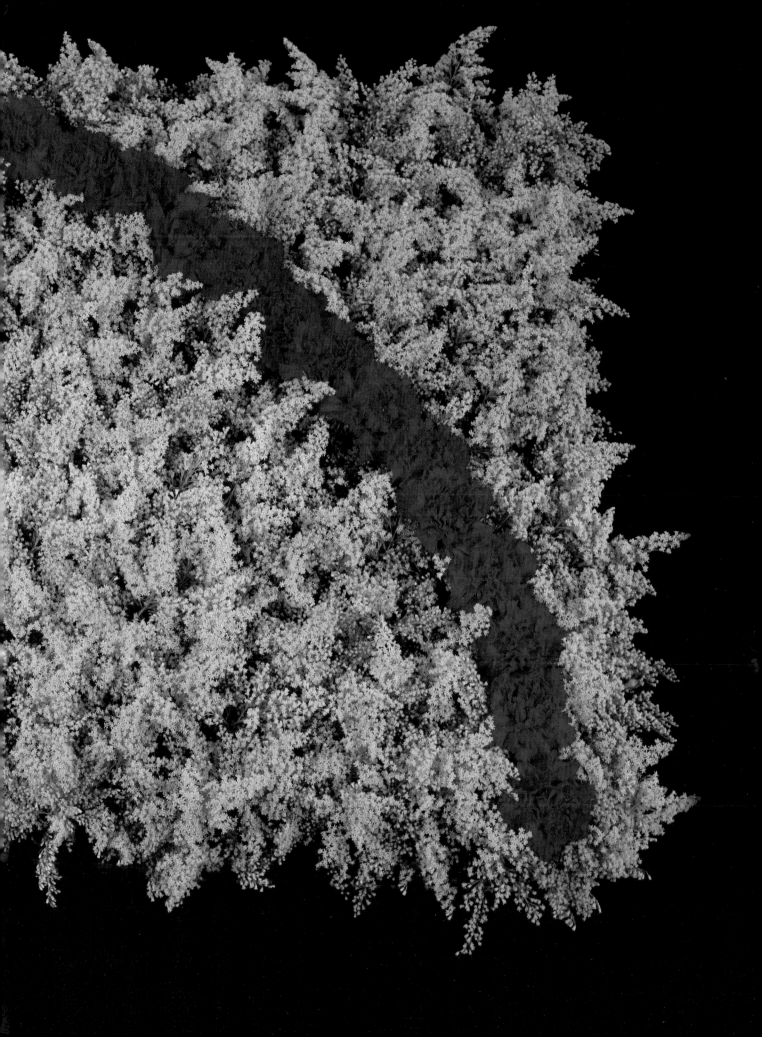

"If of thy moral goods thou art bereft

And from thy slender store two loaves

        Alone to thee are left

Sell one, and with the dole

Buy hyacinths to feed thy soul."

        Persian poet: Moslih Saadi (1300)

BIBLIOGRAPHY

Anderson, Peter G. "A Fibonacci Based Pseudo Random Number Generator," *Fibonacci Quarterly,* Vol 29, 1991.

Anderson, Peter G. *Fibonacci Numbers and Their Application.* Boston: D. Reidel Publishing, 1984.

Burke, Gobbons. "Figuring Fibonacci Retracements", *Futures,* Oct. 1993.

Crowley, Aayne E. "The Golden Section," *Psychology and Marketing,* Vol. 8, 1991.

Datson, William, Fedrick Norwood, and Charles Raylor. "Fiber Optics and Fibonacci," *Mathematics,* Vol. 66, 1993.

Doezi, Gyorgy. *The Power of Limits.* New York: Shambahala, 1981.

Evans, Brian. "Number as Form and Content, A Composer's Path of Inquiry," *Leonardo,* Vol. 25, 1992.

Evans, Helen. *Man the Designer.* New York: MacMillan and Co., 1973.

Ghyka, Matila. *The Geometry of Art and Life.* New York: Sheed and Ward, 1946.

Grimm, Richard E. "The Autobiography of Leonardo Pisano," *The Fibonacci Quarterly,* Vol. 2, 1973.

Harper Study Bible, (Revised Standard Version). Grand Rapids Michigan: Zondervan Publishing, 1962.

Huntley, H.E. *The Divine Proportion.* New York: Donor Publications, 1970.

Lawler, Robert. "The Measure of Difference," *Parabola,* Winter, 1991.

Lawler, Robert. *Sacred Geometry.* New York: Crossroads, 1982.

Lodge, Arthur. "Annals of Taxation," *Journal of Accountancy,* Vol. 163, No. 3; March 1987.

McWhinnie, Harold J. "A Biological Basis for the Golden Section in Art and Design," *Leonardo,* Vol. 22, 1992.

Moore, Randy. "Numbers of Life," *The American Biology Teacher,* February 1992.

Ochiai, T. and O. Kaiug. "Funneling Through Fibonacci Barriers," *Amercan Journal of Physics,* Vol. 58, 1990.

Peterson, Ivars. "Numbers at Random," *Science News,* Vol. 140, 1991.

Rigdon, Michael A., and Francis R. Epting. "A Test of the Golden Section Hypothesis with Elicited Constructs," *Journal of Personality and Social Psychology,* Vol. 43, Nov. 1982.

Shorter Oxford Dictionary. 1961.

Slezak, George. "How Fibonacci Can Forecast Stock Market Resistance Levels," *Futures,* Vol. 18, July 1989.

Srinivasan, T.P. "Fibonacci Sequence, Golden Ration and a Network of Resistors," *American Journal of Physics,* Vol. 60, 1992.

Stephens, Peter S. *An Introduction to Symmetry in Two Dimensions.* Cambridge, Mass.: MIT Press, 1980.

Temple, Richard, and Keith Critchlow. "The Golden Proportion," *Parabola,* Vol. 14, 1991.

Tuohy, H.P. and S.G. Estradling. "Maximum Saliance vs. Golden Section Proportions in Judgemental Assymmetry," *British Journal of Psychology,* Vol. 78, 1987.

Webster's New International, (2nd Edition). 1957.

World Book Encyclopedia, (Vol. 8). 1994.